Healing Energies of Heat and Light

ii

Healing Energies of Heat and Light

A Quantum Leap in Health Care

By Charles T. McGee MD

MediPress

Information in this book is not intended to replace services of a trained health care professional or serve as a replacement for medical care. Consult your physician or health care professional before following any proposed treatments. Any application of the methods described in this book is at the reader's discretion and sole risk.

MediPress
PO Box 5154
Coeur d'Alene ID 83814-1952 Tel: 208 664 3048

McGee, Charles T., Healing Energies of Heat and Light: A Quantum Leap in Health Care

Bibliography: pgs. 224
Includes Index.
1. Health. 2. Traditional Chinese Medicine. 3. Healing. 5. Qigong. 6. Chi Kung. 7. New Age. 8. Complementary Medicine. 9. Alternative Medicine. 10. Holistic Medicine. 11. Integrative Medicine. 12. Low Level Laser Therapy. 13. Low Level Photon Therapy. 14. Phototherapy. 15. Energy Medicine

Library of Congress Number 00-191385

ISBN 0-9636979-6-X

Printed in the United States of America (second printing 2003)

Cover by Leisa Bueno adapted from a digital photo of a *X-Light*.

ACKNOWLEDGEMENTS

Many people played a role in the development of this new healing program. First and foremost is Rodger Estes who invented the anal heater instrument, rejuvenated his terminally ill 90-year-old father in 1991, pieced together this powerful healing program, and continues to search for energy enhancing and balancing systems that produce the highest level of healing.

Thanks to the late Paul Nogier MD of France who discovered that all tissues in our bodies are in resonance with specific frequencies according to their embryologic origin. Nogier's resonance principles were transmitted through veterinarians to electrical engineer Dan Parris who began manufacturing pulsed LED (light emitting diode) equipment for animals in 1982. Over the next eighteen years a large body of therapeutic experience accumulated from observations in animals.

Thanks to Chinese qigong master Hu Jia Lai who arrived in our lives at the perfect moment. Hu shared our goal of trying to develop electronic devices that deliver healing energies as close as possible to *chi,* the healing energy of qigong masters. Hu demonstrated a remarkable healing ability and became our consultant while his energy sensitive body became a testing instrument for new designs.

Thanks to Joy Tang whose contacts with many qigong masters allowed us to receive feedback on prototypes of new designs letting us know we were headed in the right direction.

Thanks also to those who were willing to try this new approach, evaluate it on their own bodies, allow me to gain access to their medical records and tell their stories.

I also wish to thank my wife Carole for letting me pursue my rainbows and thanks go to my son Thom for his invaluable help and patience in preparation of this book.

Other books by Charles T. McGee MD

How to Survive Modern Technology
Heart Frauds
Miracle Healing From China...Qigong

Table of Contents

PREFACE

This book describes the birth of a revolution in the prevention and treatment of disease. How this program came into being is a tale stranger than fiction.

In 1977 Rodger Q. Estes invented a medical device to treat hemorrhoids with a heated probe. Going far beyond its stated indications, doctors in China tried the device in two cases of rectal cancer and the cancers disappeared. Rodger was invited to visit China where he was treated royally.

This connection led to many visits to China for me where I literally was pushed into the fascinating ancient healing discipline of qigong. Years later, in 1995, I discovered Rodger was a natural-born *qigong master,* endowed with healing abilities he never knew he had. (A qigong master is defined as a person who is able to see and sense subtle energies, emit healing energy from his hands and body and heal people with the most difficult health problems we experience.)

Rodger used his newly found abilities to search out healing products that emitted energies that felt good for his energy system. Over the next few years and from literally thousands of products he selected a small number and began using them in combination in friends, relatives and pets.

The modalities Rodger chose are simple do-it-yourself tools that don't require a prescription or a physician. Items on the list sound as if they should be unrelated; trace minerals given in the rectum or under the tongue, a niacin-flush, an unusual five-carbon sugar compound, an infrared sauna, treatment with pulsed LEDs (light emitting diodes) and the original anal heater hemorrhoid machine. Instead of results being cumulative as one might hope for, synergistic responses began to occur, some miraculous. The unbelievable observation was that almost everyone who followed the program faithfully for a reasonable time improved to some degree showing healing was being activated at a deep mysterious level in our bodies.

Theories of how this program works lead us back to the classic body energy concepts of Chinese Medicine. We believe the infrared sauna, LED devices and anal heater emit energies that help normalize resonance frequencies in the sub-atomic particles that make up our cells. Trace minerals function as catalysts for enzyme reactions in our cells and ribose may be stabilizing DNA in the body as it does in medical laboratories. Using these modalities in combination energy flow in our meridians is brought back to a state of balance and harmony and this allows innate healing abilities to wake up with a vengeance.

We are excited about this approach that offers a true method of prevention to those who are well and new hope to those who are ill. We want everyone to become aware of this discovery and benefit from its use. I hope you share my fascination with these developments as we continue to discover more about this remarkable program.

INTRODUCTION

Cells are not made up of separate parts but are a seamless web of interconnecting systems that contribute to the functional unity and healing capacity of the human body. For thousands of years, one of the core tenets of traditional Chinese medicine has been the recognition of the existence and role of energy in sickness and disease. According to Chinese medical experts, energy channels run through the entire human body and are responsible for the functioning of cells, tissues and organs. With biological networks vastly interconnected, getting a handle on this powerful entity could lead to insights into cancer and greatly diminish—or even eradicate—other long standing, chronic, multi-system illnesses.

Quantum physicists have objectively and scientifically measured how *biophotons* (tiny beams of light) interconnect the body's molecular and sub-molecular systems with meridians and acupuncture points. The importance and efficacy of acupuncture points, zones and segments as extraordinary therapeutic areas have been validated both on a scientific and clinical or empirical level. Since meridians are circuits where bio-electric, vibrating, pulsating energy flows to sustain and give life to every organ, gland and system of the body, using light energy to treat the body is like turning the key in the ignition of a car. Turning the ignition activates a whole series of events (fuel is injected, gears can be shifted, electric power is distributed to lights, radio, and air conditioning, etc). Likewise, stimulating the body's higher dimensional anatomy results in activating a multitude of biological functions.

The idea that light can illicit natural healing isn't as far-fetched as you may think. Scientists already know that patterns of daylight and darkness affect our health in surprising ways. Daily light cycles regulate basic biological rhythms in animals—making birds migrate in the fall, bears hibernate in the winter, and sows fertile in the spring. In humans these light energies—and our bodies' biological responses to them—may hold the key to unlocking the mysteries of healing and regeneration.

In *Healing Energies of Heat and Light: A Quantum Leap in Health Care*, Charles T. McGee MD leads us on a fascinating adventure into the remarkable potential of using light and other energies to balance the human energy system and augment natural healing and regeneration in the body. He begins this adventure in the early research of Paul Nogier MD of France who discovered the healing potential of light pulsed on and off and different frequencies that are related to the embryologic origin of the tissue being treated. Along the way he introduces us to Chinese Medicine and acupuncture, Chinese qigong, and German electroacupuncture. He introduces new technologies supported by the time-tested wisdom of ancient healing systems that have the potential to change the human energy system in ways that only a few years ago seemed the stuff of science fiction.

Dr. McGee lucidly describes the extraordinary potential of using light and other energies to enhance bioregulation of the body's *dynamical* energy systems. He explains how human energy systems are sensitive to inputs of various energies and how they seem to have an organizing and healing effect on the body. Today, our global ecosystem is in a fragile and unstable state due to increasing levels of worldwide pollution. Perhaps, as quantum physicists are discovering, these healing energies can make it possible to slow down or halt the cascade of chaotic energetic-molecular reactions that lead to alterations in DNA and a wide spectrum of chronic illnesses that are caused by a deteriorating natural environment.

Most compelling of all, Dr. McGee illustrates in case histories how light and other healing energies make it possible for doctors to augment immunity and slow down or prevent abnormal functions underlying chronic disease. These practices may also make it possible to build powerful immunity against the onslaught of powerful microbes that threaten the human family now and in the near future.

With increasing knowledge, scientists will undoubtedly discover that sick individuals suffer from a *mismatch* between their energetic and physical systems. The concept of a mismatch holds promise for revolutionizing our understanding of both the normal and the dysfunctional body. This mismatch involves the human energy system interface with the physical body through the *ground regulation system* or *extracellular matrix.* It is well known that the extracellular matrix is made up of crystalline structures and structured water that <u>interact</u>, <u>amplify</u> and <u>radiate</u> energy to the cellular and subcellular crystalline structures. Manipulating or fine-tuning the electromagnetic resonances of life with light and other energies that govern and regulate physiology opens up a new vista of virtually unlimited possibilities. Imagine the potential of being able to stop deranged biophysical signals from amplifying into genetic mutations that cause cancer or that wrench the emotions and derange the mind causing depression. With fewer aberrant reactions of the mind and body, the innate regulating mechanisms of the body gradually allow for a return to normal or near-normal states of functioning. As the meridian-organ connections become more proficient, the body's normal

xiii

physiological regulating systems become more resilient to stress, toxins, and infection.

As we move into the 21st century, *Healing Energies of Heat and Light: A Quantum Leap in Health Care,* is a very special achievement that provides a lucid account of humanity's unceasing effort to decode the mysteries of degenerative diseases—mysteries whose ultimate solutions grow daily more imminent.

- Paul Yanick, Jr., PhD, President of the American Academy of Quantum Medicine

CHAPTER 1: HISTORY OF THE PROGRAM

By chance the discovery was made that two energy-delivering devices could produce a synergistic healing response when used in combination. Two people who played major roles in bringing the devices together are inventor Rodger Estes of Spokane, Washington, and electrical engineer Dan Parris of Inola, Oklahoma.

Hemorrhoids Collide with a Hot Radiator

Rodger Q. Estes invented various gadgets throughout his life, usually by attempting to solve an obvious problem. His first medical discovery came in a more serendipitous way in 1977. While suffering from a severe case of hemorrhoids on a cold winter's day (bleeding, prolapse, fissures, pain from anal muscle spasms) he happened to sit on a hot steam heated radiator to look out a window. To his surprise he experienced a relief that would give the makers of *Preparation H* beautiful dreams. The inventor's light bulb of discovery burned brightly once more. From this lowly beginning came an adventure of discovery that has the potential to improve the way medicine is perceived and practiced while greatly reducing medical costs.

Rodger went to the medical library to study hemorrhoids and read surgical texts showing how they are removed. Doctors call this procedure *minor surgery,* but it most certainly is not (to doctors minor surgery is defined as surgery performed on someone else). After surgery, bowel movements must pass through an area of raw skin for weeks. This sounds worse than the rack I once saw in a dungeon in England. Personally I would prefer the rack because it might relieve my back pain (on the condition I alone was controlling the device).
Rodger researched the history of *Preparation H* discovering how a small group of cloistered nuns created the magic mix of shark oil, glycerin and bag balm. It remains a

1

mystery to this day why a little group of nuns developed a special interest in stamping out hemorrhoids. Perhaps they had little else to do and sat around eating low fiber foods.

In the 1930s the sisters placed little ads in magazines that said simply, *Hemorrhoids? Send $1.00.* In response the sufferer received a small sample of *Preparation H.* The product was a huge success, made money and eventually the sisters sold the business to more commercially minded people who probably sit around today counting their money while eating low fiber foods and growing hemorrhoids.

Rodger made a prototype heater and asked several hemorrhoid surgeons if they would try it out. It should have come as no surprise when not one was interested. Finally a friendly obstetrician tested the heater as a personal favor.

The test case was a woman with huge hemorrhoids who was five months pregnant. Rodger did not personally see these hemorrhoids but the obstetrician told him the cluster measured over three inches in diameter. If the hemorrhoids had been painted a different color they could have resembled a rose.

The poor woman was so miserable she spent most of the time lying down with the foot of the bed elevated. Every time she stood up blood pooled into the hemorrhoids causing them to swell. She couldn't perform the normal tasks of caring for her family such as shopping and going out for fast food. This would be a truly challenging trial case even for a seasoned old gynecologist like me.

In the privacy of the exam room the doctor placed the tiny probe into the middle of this flower shaped cluster and began the treatment. To the amazement of the doctor and his assistant the hemorrhoids shrank 90 percent within ten minutes. No one anticipated any response this dramatic and word spread from one doctor to another, then outside the medical community to venture capitalists who saw dollar signs flash on and off.

Before long a corporation was formed that rapidly sold $3 million of stock in a public offering. Rodger obtained a patent on the device and the company pushed ahead with clinical trials in both the United States and Japan to get clearance from the FDA to market the device with medical indications. The timing appeared to be perfect for Rodger because his royalties from previous inventions were dwindling.

(See photo of the prototype hemorrhoid device in the photo section)

Relief of BPH Symptoms (Benign Prostatic Hypertrophy)

More serendipity occurred in clinical trials of the device. The very first patient to take a machine home was called the next day for a phone report. Yes, the heater had relieved his hemorrhoids very well. This answer was wonderful and fit into the question and answer squares on research forms. However, something even more impressive occurred. The man slept through the night for the first time in years, not being forced to get up to urinate the usual six times because of his enlarged prostate.

The trial period for each volunteer was short and soon the gentleman was asked to return the instrument. He asked if he could buy the device but was told he couldn't because it was not yet on the market and hadn't received FDA clearance. Therefore the only course of action was to return it. Then he said he would pay $2,000 for the device and shoot anyone who came out to his farm to try to take it away. It was almost harvest time and he didn't want to look forward to sitting on his hemorrhoids in his combine fourteen hours a day making frequent stops to urinate on the wheat stubble.

When the clinical trials were concluded, efforts moved to marketing. The FDA cleared the device on a prescription-only basis and that crippled sales. The setback turned out to be but one of several blows for the little company as almost every management decision turned out to be fatal as well.

A final effort was made to get the FDA to authorize the sale of the device without a prescription. This was accomplished when a company representative met with an FDA official in a car outside the FDA building. Then, after all the effort to conduct clinical trials

Rodger found an old 1936 article from Johns Hopkins School of Medicine published in the *Journal of Urology* describing treatment of infections of the prostate with a heated probe. The hemorrhoid machine could have been grand fathered (cleared for use by being in existence before device regulations were placed in effect in 1976) saving study costs that added up to $100,000.

The article described a long metal tube that was placed far enough up the rectum to rest on the prostate. Hot water from an external source was pumped through channels in the tube. A high rate of success was reported in the treatment of prostatitis, a chronic infection of the gland that remains an enigma for urologists even today because antibiotics don't easily pass from the blood into the prostate.

The instrument was made by the Elliot Treatment Regulator Company. The treatment did not catch on and soon the little company was history. The first effort to successfully manufacture an anal heater failed and history was about to repeat itself.

The new little company went bankrupt and several years passed before the remaining devices and parts were legally transferred to Rodger. By 1985 he had a few thousand devices and a locker full of parts, but no sales. Then another odd twist to this story occurred.

Enter The Dragon

While the little company was in business a salesman left two machines in China as samples. He very likely dreamed the Chinese would start buying devices by the tens of millions, the usual pipe dream of people trying to do business in China.

The instruments were first used on high-ranking government officials who were scheduled for hemorrhoid surgery. All of them improved and were able to cancel surgery. Being able to dodge a bullet like that makes a person eternally grateful, so Rodger immediately had friends in high places.

The Chinese are famous for innovation so they must have thought, "If the anal heater helps hemorrhoids why not see what else it can do?" Soon they found it relieved symptoms of prostatitis and benign prostate enlargement (BPH). If it could do that why not go all the way and see what it might do with cancer?

They used the instrument first on a patient whose rectal cancer had returned following surgery. To the surprise of all the cancer shrank and disappeared completely! After that success they tried it on a second rectal cancer patient who was newly diagnosed and had not started treatment. Lightning struck again and that cancer disappeared as well.

That's when Rodger got a letter (in Chinese) from Dr. Stephen Kong and off to Beijing he went to talk business. While in China he met with officials of health providers of large government-owned industries. He went back to China, and back, and back again. During his visits Rodger told his contact about alternative treatment methods I used in my medical practice. Dr. Kong immediately saw similarities with Traditional Chinese Medicine and during a visit to the United States invited me to give several lectures to medical groups in China.

Millions of Americans have gone to China since it invited President Nixon to visit. Most stay in high priced luxury hotels and are herded around in tour buses with English speaking guides. During our trips Rodger and I were fortunate to have our own personal guide and translator in Dr. Kong (we never did understand why Kong chose to write his letter to Rodger in Chinese because he speaks excellent English). We were wined and dined and introduced to movers and shakers at high levels in many fields. I once was the guest of honor at a banquet given by the city manager of Beijing where I had to figure out how to eat a foot long shrimp with chopsticks as everyone watched and waited (by tradition the guest of honor begins to eat first). We highly recommend this way to see China if you can arrange it.

One of the highlights for Rodger on this trip was a visit to a prostate disease clinic in a large hospital in Beijing. The clinic consisted of a large open room with fifty examination tables and no privacy. Each table was designed so that when the patient lay on his stomach a crank could be turned that bent the body at the waist thrusting the buttocks toward the ceiling. This made it easy for the doctor to pass from patient to patient performing rectal exams on all fifty bottoms in short order. Possibly world speed records were being set as written notes were not required and jasmine tea was steeping in the adjacent lounge.

The doctor was also salaried at $50 per month in 1987 so a pleasant bedside manner was not needed. At that time even coronary bypass surgeons were paid $50 per month, not much of an incentive to do the procedures and few were done. By contrast nurses made $30 per month and street sweepers $18.

Rodger didn't take his camera that day and what a photo opportunity he missed! Fifty bare bottoms pointed to the sky in neat military-style rows. Developing a visual image of this may seem comical, but just wait. If we don't find some way to control run-away health care costs, managed care systems may cause you one day to find your own bare bottom in a sea of bare bottoms pointed at the sky, possibly in a unisex environment as well.

After an enjoyable month the excursion ended poorly for Rodger. He was led to believe thousands of hemorrhoid machines were going to be purchased. The Oil Service Industry, fully owned and controlled by the Government of China, backed out of a letter of intent claiming lack of funds albeit at a time of huge trade surpluses for China. At the least Rodger expected to receive payment for the 130 machines already delivered to this group. He got nothing. Disappointed he broke off his contact with Dr. Kong vowing never to be burned in China again (he did return six years later and got burned once more). In contrast the trip did go well for me and this led to a second trip, then four more.

An Introduction to Body Energies and Qigong

One day during my first trip in 1987 Dr. Kong arranged for me to meet a 70 year old western-trained MD. For several years Dr. Li Lau-Shi practiced western style medicine in a hospital in

Beijing, prescribing the common western drugs and recommending surgery when indicated. When he was thirty-five Dr. Li had polio that left him paralyzed below the waist. For the next fifteen years he practiced medicine in a wheel chair. During that time he developed severe high blood pressure that failed to respond to western drug therapy. He also had recurrent pneumonias, each more life threatening than the last.

At age 50 he was admitted to the hospital with pneumonia that failed to respond to anything his western physician friends could offer. His doctor told him he was expected to die and he should say good-bye to family members. Instead he decided to practice qigong exercises.

Because he couldn't get out of bed and there was nothing else to do (no TV sets) he practiced qigong exercises (breathing and mental) almost every waking hour. Over the next few months he cured himself of everything. His blood pressure returned to normal without drugs, he had no more episodes of pneumonia and even the paralysis of fifteen years went away gradually. After this miraculous response Dr. Li gave up the practice of western style medicine to become a teacher of qigong. Early every morning for the past ten years he taught qigong with great agility in a park to 300 to 400 students (he couldn't teach qigong during the Cultural Revolution because it was banned).

My visit with Dr. Li took place in the apartment of a conventional western trained surgeon who assured me this amazing story was 100% accurate. The doctor in question worked at the same hospital in which Dr. Li was admitted time after time and seen in the outpatient clinic. All the medical records for his entire life were in one chart about four inches thick. In addition, his miraculous recovery occurred right under the noses of his western-trained medical friends. Those skeptical doctors came to accept the facts as valid even though none could offer an explanation for the miraculous recovery. Over my next five trips to China I heard similar comments over and over from Chinese western-trained doctors who repeatedly said there is something positive happening with qigong healing.

Dr. Li placed his hand over mine. I could feel great heat radiating from his hand, similar to placing your hand too close to an electric heater. When Dr. Kong asked him to turn over his hand I saw his palm had an unusual color distribution resembling a target. An area about two inches in diameter in the center of the palm was white. The remainder of the hand and fingers were flushed red. This was not the last time I was to gaze on a palm with this unusual color pattern.

I came away bewildered by the experience and didn't know what to think about the experience. It certainly didn't compute in my western brain so I buried it away very deeply hoping it would get lost. The experience came back later in spades.

I returned to China the next year (1988), largely to see if it were possible to develop a medication for jet lag using the hormone melatonin that we could sell in international airports. I was in love with melatonin because it blocked jet lag I normally experienced that made me dread overseas travel.

During this trip Dr. Kong literally forced me into learning about Qigong. Qigong is a 4,000 year-old healing method that was kept a close secret among emperors, their doctors, monks and the intellectual elite for thousands of years. Great healing responses were reported, even in cases of cancer and paralysis following stroke and spinal cord severances. Only in the 1980s did the government allow qigong classes to be held in public. Interest in qigong was growing and scientists were performing qigong research studies in institutions of higher learning all over the country. Along with this explosion of interest several international congresses were held to share this knowledge with the world.

By 1993 over 900 scientific papers had been presented, abstracted and translated into English (according to Dr. Kenneth Sancier of the Qigong Institute, the number is now over 1,600). Basic science studies were being done on high-level qigong *masters* with verified healing records. But that is another story. Suffice it to say my inquiries led to the writing of a book with qigong master Effie Poy Yew Chow PhD RN of San Francisco, *Miracle Healing From China...Qigong.*

8

Additional Uses

After learning about the cure of two people with rectal cancer in China, Rodger began trying the heater on a variety of symptoms and conditions. The cancer cures caused him to suspect anal heat might somehow stimulate the immune system. When a neighbor complained to Rodger of his life long hay fever problem, he recommended the heater. The neighbor took one long treatment, had the worst flare-up of his life (people in natural healing call this a healing crisis) and has not suffered from hay fever since 1990.

Then came the miraculous recovery of Rodger's stepfather. I saw Hank in my office in 1989 when he was 89 years old but was unable to help him. He had psoriasis over 40% of his body and could barely move his fingers because of arthritis as well as many other common conditions to old age.

In 1991 Rodger's stepfather Hank was hospitalized for congestive heart failure with a massively enlarged heart. The cardiologist told Rodger he would treat him with drugs but didn't expect the old man to live more than a week or two. He was sent home to die but Rodger had other plans.

Hank had an enlarged prostate that caused him to get up five or six times a night to urinate. He used the heater that evening and slept through the night like a baby. Rodger took Hank's lab tests to a biochemist for a chemistry balancing. Within three months all of his health problems were going away! Hank celebrated his 100th birthday in December of 1999, and bowled a 192 game a month later. This is an ongoing story and his tale of rejuvenation is presented in Chapter 3.

Rodger was on alert, ready to try the heater on agreeable souls both animal and human. When a veterinarian told him he should put his aging dog *Panda* to sleep (Panda was named long before the China trips) because of kidney failure (markedly elevated BUN at 302 and no urine output), Rodger took the dog home. He held Panda on his lap and gave her a treatment with the

9

heater. The dog came back to normal function the next day and lived for two more weeks before dying peacefully in her sleep.

Around that time a friend of ours asked Rodger if he had a cure for a horse that had four to five inch hives all over its body for a month. The veterinarian had no more ideas so Rodger put his inventive mind to work. His son had a machine shop so Rodger asked him to machine tool a larger version of the anal heater. Three days later Rodger held the heater in the horse's anus for 40 minutes. The next morning the hives were gone permanently and the horse was playfully running around the pasture.

Qigong Master Rodger?

Rodger read my qigong book when it appeared in 1994 and took a casual interest in the subject. Soon this story was about to take yet another strange turn.

As I was leaving Rodger's home one day in 1995 he waved good-bye to me with his hand raised and open. I glanced at his palm with shock. Rodger's palm had a color pattern similar to those of qigong masters I had seen in China. An area about two inches in diameter in the middle of his palm was white and this area was surrounded by red flushed skin. I pointed this out to him and he looked at his palm with surprise. This is how Rodger discovered he had natural abilities to heal with his hands without putting in the usual lifetime of exercises and practice. He blames me for his continued involvement in body energies and healing because it was I who discovered he was a natural-born qigong master. As he jokingly says, "It's all your fault, Charlie!"

Retirement?

In 1995, at the age of 65, Rodger was planning to retire and live on sales of his anal heaters. He regularly attended a variety of unusual meetings, health fairs, whole life expos, etc., trying to sell a few anal heaters and looking for promising new healing methods and devices. With his newly found qigong abilities he discovered he could hold his hand near a bottle of pills or liquid, any object or device offered for sale, and feel good, bad, or neutral energy vibrations coming from the product. After trying this procedure on literally thousands of items he sifted out a tiny number of gems.

The first was a red light emitting diode (LED). From 200 feet across the sales area of a health meeting he saw Pamela Baker-Olszewski holding a single red LED above her head. Almost mesmerized by the red light he made his way across the auditorium, met Pam and pulled out his checkbook. Pam and her electrical engineer husband, David, operate a company called *Light Energy Inc* out of Seattle as a side business. They manufacture LED devices and sell them at health related shows all over the country (see Resources appendix).

At another meeting Rodger saw a small neoprene pad containing several red LEDs. He placed his hand over the device, felt good vibes, and out came the checkbook again. At a later meeting he sat in an infrared sauna, liked what he felt and bought a unit. Armed with these new toys he began to experiment first on himself as usual, then on friends.

Nearing 70 Rodger decided to end his quest for new ideas. He planned to sell off his remaining anal heater units and future business prospects and retire with Hank to the Greek island of Kos, home of Hippocrates, the *father* of medicine. In late 1998 he was off to Greece to look at property.

Rodger was on friendly terms with his former wife, Lisa, a Greek woman who had returned to Athens after the divorce. Lisa tried to arrange travel to Kos but a series of severe storms made it impossible to travel on many days and tickets were sold out when the weather improved.

Rodger turned his attention to trying to track down the closely guarded secret intravenous cancer formula used on his sister in the late 1970s by Greek biochemist Hariton Tzannis Alivizatos, PhD. On two visits to Athens, six months apart, Gloria temporarily returned from death's door to a condition of useful enjoyable life. The biochemist died during an epileptic seizure at the young age of 44 in the early 1990s apparently taking his secrets to the grave with him.

Rodger spent two weeks in Greece and never did get to Kos. He took this as a signal to change his plans and stay in Spokane and active in the area of healing.

In the summer of 1999 his healing efforts began to change in a dramatic way. He continued to have people use his anal heater but added a trace mineral mix (given rectally), a niacin-flush, oral d-ribose, a 30-minute infrared sauna, and the use of a two-foot long pulsed LED blanket made for dogs. The combination sounds ridiculous at face value but the results show a powerful synergistic healing effect can occur. When Rodger told me how well people responded I checked out his toughest cases (by requesting and reviewing copies of medical records), confirmed his stories, and returned from retirement to participate, hence this book.

CHAPTER 2: A PARALLEL HISTORY

In the early 1970s the word *acupuncture* was working its way into the vocabulary of Americans. As soon as China opened training courses in acupuncture to Americans in about 1972, Ohio veterinarian Marvin Cain packed his bag for an extended trip. Dr. Cain learned human acupuncture, made adaptations for animals and went on to developed new diagnostic and treatment skills far superior to those used by animal acupuncturists in China. Frequently these special tools allowed him to succeed where standard veterinary approaches failed. He is referred to as the *father of equine acupuncture* and authored the book *Acupuncture Diagnosis and Treatment of the Equine (*1996). Every spring he can be found getting horses in shape for Triple Crown events such as the Kentucky Derby.

In the late 1970s Lloyd McKibbin DVM of Wheatley, Ontario, Canada, traveled to France to study with Paul Nogier MD, the father of *ear medicine* and *ear acupuncture*. Because of this contact Dr. Nogier visited Canada several times to teach his methods and through that contact Dr. Cain learned of his discoveries.

Dan Parris of Oklahoma is another principal player in this story. While Dan worked in the aerospace industry as an electrical engineer a chiropractor friend began to study acupuncture. Someone in the class had a small electrical acupuncture stimulator from China and everybody wanted one. Dan supplied the class with duplicates of the instrument and later left the aerospace industry to develop a business manufacturing acupuncture devices.

During the 1960s *soft,* or *cold*, lasers (lasers using doses too low to damage tissues) were being used in Europe to alleviate pain and stimulate acupuncture points. Dan followed this development with interest but only from a business point of view. Although making a living manufacturing electronic acupuncture devices he remained skeptical about the usefulness of acupuncture treatments themselves.

13

Terminology Problems

This is a good time to clear up confusion that may arise from use of the word *laser*. A laser is a *coherent* (sticking together or concentrated) beam of one wavelength of light that delivers enough energy for enough time to cut or burn. Lasers are used as cutting tools in industry and in medical applications such as burning off warts and the treatment of retinal detachments.

Laser researchers discovered if they reduced power delivered to the body to non-injurious levels between 1 to 300 Joules per square centimeter of skin surface (a Joule is the equivalent of 1 watt-second) beneficial responses were observed. Treatment with these low doses of light is currently being referred to by several terms such as low-level *laser* therapy (LLLT), low-intensity *laser* therapy (LILT), low-energy *laser* therapy (LELT) and low-level photon therapy (LLPT).

In searching the National Library of Medicine on the Internet I found studies under all of these headings in addition to others. Most articles are accumulating under the heading of Low Level Laser Therapy (LLLT) and where research studies in that area are quoted in this book that term will be used. To date most studies published have used true lasers with the power turned down to safe levels, but there are exceptions to this statement.

Use of the word *laser* is not really appropriate here. When low-levels of laser energy hit the skin the light energy spreads in all directions and most of its *coherency* is lost. Dr. Pekka J Pontinen PhD, MD, a world expert in this new field of therapy, wrote a text called *Low Level Laser Therapy* in 1992 but now believes the term low-energy *photon* therapy (LEPT) is more appropriate. That term may be meaningful for people with a background in physics but I doubt most readers of this book will relate to the word *photon* except through terms applied to the weaponry of the starship *Enterprise* on *Star Trek*. A photon is defined as a quantum of electromagnetic energy having both the character of a particle and the character of a wave.

14

About 20 years ago it was discovered that the same beneficial effects seen with LLLT (LEPT) could be achieved with light emitting diodes (LEDs) without using the more expensive true lasers. LEDs are capable of delivering power levels in the same range as LLLT and responses in body tissues appear to be the same. A small number of published and unpublished studies report positive biologic effects with non-coherent wavelengths (non-laser light energy). These can be found in references 26, 27, 30, 31, 32, 33, 34 and 35 in Appendix III.

LED devices have obvious advantages over lasers because they are cheaper, safer and available on a non-prescription basis (not doctor controlled like lasers). Whenever I describe herein a treatment response in a client using Rodger's program LEDs were used, not LLLT.

Paralyzed Old Dog Walking

Dr. Cain invited Dan Parris to come to Ohio and observe the use of a pulsed cold laser therapy unit manufactured by Dan's company. The patient, an old paralyzed dog, received a treatment, got up and walked out of the room. Not long afterward Dan saw another traumatically paralyzed dog walk after being treated with acupuncture. In China this kind of result is reported and observed in humans and in 1990 I saw a paralyzed woman improve when she was treated by a Chinese acupuncturist in San Francisco.

Dan was interested in the human application of acupuncture but decided to restrict his work to veterinary medicine. At the time the FDA had a very negative attitude toward acupuncture and related devices and customs officials had orders to seize acupuncture needles and devices from travelers even though similar items could be purchased in the United States. Dan was also aware that the FDA did not regulate devices for use in animals.

Technology was changing rapidly and red and infrared LEDs (light emitting diodes) were on the market. In 1982 Dan manufactured a pad of infrared LEDs pulsed at Nogier's

15

frequencies. Prior to that time true laser instruments were so bulky and heavy only a strong man could lift and aim the laser for treatment. In 1988 he was granted a patent for a very portable pulsed infrared LED device (including the pad design) that veterinarians were using to accelerate various healing processes as successfully and sometimes more so than the laser devices they used previously.

Corneal Ulcers in Race Horses

Dr. Cain told me how he now spends most of his time treating racehorses and many suffer corneal injuries during races when mud, dirt and rocks are kicked back into their faces. If you are a racehorse there is a definite advantage to running up front. When a horse suffers such an injury it returns to the stable with one eye shut and watering.

In 1982 Dr. Cain used Dan's pad with 16-pulsed infrared LEDs (confusingly identified by the trademarked name of Lacer that sounds like laser) to treat a horse with a corneal ulcer for the first time. He selected frequency A, covered the closed eye with the pad for *a minute or two* with the power on and a short while later checked the cornea. To his amazement he could see edges of the ulcer beginning to heal in as he watched.

By the next morning the healing process was proceeding so rapidly he said it *shook him up*. Since then he has treated hundreds of corneal ulcers in animals with similar results. He says prior to 1982 when small animals suffered corneal injuries he sewed the inner eyelid closed and most cases took about a week to heal. With pulsed LEDs he no longer sews the lid shut because the healing is so rapid.

Both Dan Parris and Dr. Cain give credit to Paul Nogier for discovering the benefits of using specific frequencies of pulsed light on different tissues in the body.

16

I Remember Nogier Well

Hearing Nogier's name brought back memories of trips I made to Lyon, France, to attend his courses in 1975 and 1976. Nogier began by refreshing our memories of embryology (how our bodies develop from a fertilized egg in the uterus) in which three basic embryologic tissues (ectoderm, endoderm and mesoderm) develop into all parts of our bodies.

The basis for Nogier's discovery is a pulse test that is very different than used in Chinese Medicine (See Chapter 7 for more details). Using this new test he found that tissues derived from these three embryologic origins are in *resonance* with specific frequencies that just happen to be harmonics of the musical note *D.* He found other harmonics of the musical note D (given as pulsed light) had healing effects as well and eventually ended up working with Sedat (Societe d'Etudes et d'Applications Techniques, a local electronics manufacturing firm near Lyon, France), designing electronic instruments that delivered his seven pulsed energies in a variety of ways.

He found that an injured or diseased organ or tissue frequently improves or heals rapidly when exposed to its normal resonance frequency. Using his new tools Nogier delivered a steady stream of remarkable recoveries in difficult cases. These are the types of cases doctors don't like to discuss and you don't see examples of them on TV shows that glorify successes of modern medicine. Doctors refer to such people as *treatment failures* and wish they would go away. You don't want to be one.

In the early 1980s few veterinarians were aware of this equipment and most LED devices were sold directly to owners of racehorses, barrel racers and show horses. One such owner was a scientist who was very curious about the healing properties of pulsed LEDs.

Tissue Culture Cancer Cell Studies

About 1984 Priscilla Strang PhD, a neurophysiologist and researcher at the University of Miami School of Medicine, told Dan she wanted to perform some basic research using pulsed infrared LEDs (*not* low level laser therapy). She was using Dan's pulsed LEDs on her horses and observed that injuries healed much more rapidly than normal.

The easiest and cheapest step was to use materials available to her at work. She decided to work with tissue cultures of mouse myeloma cancer cells (a form of bone cancer). Cancer cells were placed in a petri dish and exposed to pulsed infrared LEDs. Dan custom made a device for the study containing 30 diodes in 3 square inches to fit the top of the lab dish. Different samples of the mouse cancer cells were exposed to Nogier's seven frequencies for 5, 10, or 20 minutes.

Several interesting things were observed. At all seven frequencies the pH of the media fell (became more acid). With the A (292 Hz) and B (584 Hz) frequencies bubbling occurred without a rise in temperature, apparently from some chemical reaction.

Growth rate of the cancer cells was slowest with the E frequency (4,672 Hz) but time of exposure was important as well. Growth rate of cells was 23% of that observed in untreated controls at five minutes, 19% at ten minutes, then *increased* to 42% at 20 minutes. Therefore, at the most effective frequency (E) 10 minutes of exposure was more beneficial than 20 minutes! Frequency F (73 Hz) had no effect on the growth rate.

In the second group of studies human nerve cancer cells (neuroblastoma) were treated with the seven frequencies for fifteen minutes per day for a week. Similar results were seen but only frequency A (292 Hz) was effective. This is consistent with Nogier's findings because nerve tissue comes from ectoderm that is in resonance with frequency A. With exposure to the LEDs, cancer cells became more normal (more differentiated ---- looking more like they should) and there was less cancer gene activity (N-Myco oncogene expression decreased).

This was a powerful study and a larger abstract on the mouse cancer cell study is included as reference #33 in Appendix III. The study was presented at the 6th Congress of the International Society for Laser Surgery and Medicine, Jerusalem, Israel, October 13-18, 1985. Dan Parris presented the paper because Dr. Strang was unable to attend.

Up to this point the research was done inexpensively. Dr. Strang wanted to enlarge on this impressive beginning and submitted a request for funding to a private foundation (she requested all of $25,944 per year for two years). The application was turned down in 1988 and the work stopped.

Someone Was Jealous of Success

A few weeks after Dr. Strang's paper was presented to the laser congress in Israel officials from the United States Attorney General's office entered Dan's factory (in Oklahoma) with an arrest warrant for his LED devices (not for him!). Officials had a search warrant to look for any studies he may be performing illegally on humans without official clearance and approval. The Attorney General's Office apparently had statements from individuals that the infrared LED devices did nothing, were worthless, and Dan knew this. Therefore his company was selling "snake oil" and committing fraud.

After discovering what his legal defense costs might be, Dan could not afford to hire an attorney even though all the accusations were false. A default judgment was issued and the feds seized his records and $35,000 of LED devices.

A few years later Dan met a stranger who filled in the rest of the story. A jealous researcher at an unidentified university filed a false complaint because of fears that someone else might be getting close to discovering a breakthrough in cancer.

Dan later resumed manufacturing pulsed LED devices for horses and small animals and continues to do so. This is the source of the blankets of pulsed red LEDs Rodger was using in 1999 when he was developing his program (it is perfectly legal for

19

an individual to use an animal product on himself if he so chooses).

Dan offers a possible explanation of why cells may respond to pulsed light from a physics viewpoint. He says atoms and molecules have resonance charges that affect their structure and anything, such as trace mineral deficiencies and environmental factors, can alter this resonance charge. After a period of time changes in these charges and structures become fixed. He theorizes that intermittent treatment with pulsed light can retrain these delinquent atoms and molecules and get them to return to the structure and resonance they had when they were normal.

He offers an analogy to clarify this idea. If you strike a tuning fork that is caked with dried mud the tuning fork will vibrate but at an altered resonance frequency. Each time you strike the tuning fork you might knock a bit of the dried mud free and this may eventually allow its vibration to return to normal (a healed state). If the mud is fresh and wet (as in a new illness) the tuning fork can throw off the mud easily and return to normal resonance more quickly (a healed condition).

For many years I gave a similar answer to patients when asked questions like, "Why me, doctor? What did I do to get this disease, I haven't done anything different?" or "Why can't any doctor fix me?" I frequently used the analogy that when a person's electromagnetic system is hit hard enough it goes on *tilt* similar to when a pinball machine is bumped too hard. A lot of effort may be needed to get out of the *tilt* condition and it may stay in that mode until power is turned off (death).

Dan sent me the transcript of a December 19, 1995, episode of the NBC-TV News-show *Dateline* in which Jane Pauley introduced the story of a man who developed tremors in his hands from cerebral palsy. His doctor advised him to take up a musical instrument that required use of both hands believing such physical therapy would be beneficial. The man took up the harp and found if he played the instrument every three days his hands didn't

20

shake. If he didn't practice again within three days the tremors and spasms resumed.

Dan says when this man placed the frame of the harp against the bones of his shoulder musical vibrations were transmitted throughout his body all the way to his toes. He speculates this must have normalized the resonance frequency of his nervous system for a three-day period every time he practiced.

Pulsed LEDs and Diabetes

Dan Parris directed me to his production manager, electrical engineer Dave Melone, who told me of the use of pulsed LED devices in three diabetics. The first diabetic was a long time friend who had been on insulin since age 22. Dave showed him how to use blankets of pulsed LEDs for full body coverage. Blood sugars fell from 200-250 down to normal (90-130) as he decreased his insulin dose (making no other changes). The man did not follow a good diet or good health habits and for unexplained reasons stopped the trial after only four or five uses (cost was not a factor as it was free).

The second diabetic was a neighbor who was taking pills for diabetes. This gentleman used the pulsed red LED blankets only three times over the course of one week and his blood sugars of 200-270 fell to 80 in the morning and 120-140 after meals. This man also discontinued this simple treatment even though it cost him nothing and good results came quickly.

The third diabetic was Dave's father-in-law who developed diabetes in 1992 at the age of 56. Three years later he began to develop skin ulcers on his shins following minor bumps that normally should not cause injury. The ulcers usually were about two inches in diameter and wouldn't heal. This is a problem in diabetics caused by poor circulation. He also showed early signs of loss of feeling in his feet, a condition called *diabetic neuropathy.*

He began to use pads of pulsed infrared LEDs about a year after the ulcer problem began. Soon he found that new traumatic ulcers on his legs healed easily and the neurologic

21

symptoms cleared up as well. He told me he is very impressed with what can be done with his pulsed LED device. He uses it to relieve arthritic and other aches and pains and his wife also uses it to relieve minor pains.

Dave related the case of a lady who had surgery for a leg fracture. As a test she used the pulsed LED blanket on one part of her scar. The treated area healed much better with less scar formation and no discoloration after several weeks compared to the untreated area.

Another lady with systemic lupus erythematosis (SLE) used pulsed LED blankets successfully to relieve aches and pains so common with that condition.

Through a second party Dave heard of a man with multiple sclerosis who tried the pulsed LED blankets. After being unable to leave his home for three years the gentleman returned to work in the office full time.

Dave says pulsed LEDs have the ability to stop the blister reflex in burns and allow them to heal with little soreness. The secret of success with burns is to have a blanket on hand in the home (in the first aid kit) and begin to treat the burn within minutes. Once Dave stumbled near the kitchen range and his hand slipped into a pot of boiling vegetable oil (400 degrees F). He immediately covered the hand with a pulsed LED blanket. He suffered little pain and experienced no blistering. Dave's father-in-law told me one of his grandchildren once backed into a fire with skin exposed. With use of the pulsed LED pad no blistering occurred and pain was minimal.

Dan Parris told me of his aunt who lived with chronic hepatitis for several years. He gave her a pulsed LED pad to use over her liver with instructions to set it on Nogier's frequency for endoderm (584 Hz). She did so for a couple of weeks and all of her discomfort and borderline jaundice cleared. She took the pad home with her and whenever symptoms begin to recur she uses the pad and the problem clears up.

Research With LLLT

Therapy with low levels of light energy is about 20 years old and a scientific literature has been accumulating documenting beneficial effects in animals and humans. Positive effects of low-level laser therapy (using the same doses of light energy delivered by LEDs) from the book *Low Level Laser Therapy* (1988) by Ohshiro and Calderhead include the following:
1. An increase in vascularity of skin flaps in rats (improved circulation for healing).
2. Regeneration of nerves to skin after the skin was undercut (in mice). Nerves grew back to treated skin areas at higher rates than to untreated areas. Nogier's frequencies were used. (A study by Lloyd McKibbon DVM of Canada)
3. Relief of the pain of trigeminal neuralgia (human).
4. Healing in skin grafts that previously failed to heal (human).
5. A reduction in hyperpigmentation (human).
6. Hemangiomas (discolored growths of blood vessels) shrank and disappeared (human).
7. Moles disappeared (human).
8. Areas of vitiligo (loss of pigment in the skin) returned to normal.

Dr. Pontinen described additional positive responses in the book *Complementary and Alternative Veterinary Medicine* (1998). Beneficial responses of *LEPT* (Low Energy Photon Therapy, or LLLT) included the following:
1. An increase in the activity of fibroblasts (cells that do repair work in the body).
2. An increase in collagen formation (a material that holds tissues together).
3. An increase in phagocytosis by white blood cells (a part of the immune defense system in which white blood cells literally eat up bacteria, viruses and debris).
4. Shortened wound healing time.

5. Anti-inflammatory effects.
6. Increased regeneration of skeletal muscles in rats.
7. Increased strength of tendons that are cut and sutured in research studies in rabbits. (This result also was seen in an unpublished study in rabbits funded by Dan Parris. While control tendons easily pulled apart, tendons treated with LEDs healed so strongly by 21 days they pulled out of bony attachments when enough tension was applied).
8. Effectiveness in first aid treatment in minor injuries such as wounds scratches and burns (Dr. Pontinen told Dan Parris he thinks LEPT devices should be present in every first aid kit).
9. Shortened healing time of fractures.
10. Shortened healing time for many types of sports injuries.
11. Increased synthesis of DNA.
12. Increased synthesis of ATP (used in the body for energy transfer in cells).
13. Increased protein synthesis.
14. Accelerated skin growth and prevention of keloids (excessive scar formation) following burns.
15. Effectively treated herpes simplex (cold sores).
16. Relieved symptoms in people with ankylosing spondylitis (rheumatoid arthritis of the spine).
17. Relieved symptoms of osteoarthritis (but not in the hip).
18. Helped 60% of people with post-herpetic neuralgia (pain after shingles that does not go away).

Osteomyelitis

One report from Spain is of exceptional interest. A 49 year-old man suffered infections (osteomyelitis) in both tibias (the long weight bearing bones of the shins) since he was five. Various attempts to heal the infections had been made through the years.

Doctors concentrated treatment on the right leg and the final step included a skin graft followed by sixteen treatments with LLLT. While observing progressive healing of the graft on the right leg doctors were surprised to find the infection in the left leg healed completely, including a fistula tract. The investigators called this a "remote laser effect." (*Investigacion y Clinica Laser* 2;94, 1985, in Spanish). This is a most remarkable result. Orthopedic surgeons fear osteomyelitis (bone infections) because it is very difficult to heal as demonstrated by the life-long problem this man experienced. Many cases end with amputations. This type of generalized healing response demonstrates why many animal studies that have attempted to use an opposite extremity as a control often do not come out as expected.

A recent paper attempted to analyze why some reports on LLLT failed to show benefits. Thirty-five negative double-blind studies (reporting the treatment didn't work) were selected from over 1,200 published studies. In some cases an obvious under-dosing was apparent. In others necessary information was missing that would allow researchers to evaluate a study, such as wavelength of light used, power, power at tissue, type of pulsing, pulse frequency, power density and total dose of light energy. The authors even made the unusual effort to write letters to several researchers asking for missing information but they received no replies (*J Clinical Laser Medicine and Surgery* 16;245-248, 1998).

More selected studies showing beneficial results from low energy light therapy can be found in Appendix III.

I asked Dan Parris if he ever heard of a complication with LED treatment and he said he knew of only one. A racehorse fractured a splint bone, a non-weight bearing bone in its front leg. A trainer treated the painful area with LEDs using the E frequency for pain; the horse stopped limping and raced again. The limp returned after the next two races and each time the horse seemed to respond favorably to the E frequency. After the next race the limp returned, an X-ray was taken and not even the beginning signs of healing were found. The trainer stopped using frequency E, switched to the B and C frequencies and the bone healed normally.

25

In the fall of 1999 Rodger, Dan, Dave and I became acquainted, shared similar success stories of healing and began to work together. This was the beginning of a period of cross education and progress that continues to this day.

CHAPTER 3: THE REJUVENATION OF HANK

Hank's story is one of the highlights of this healing quest in many ways. At night when my *western* trained brain slips back into skepticism I focus on the remarkable recovery of Rodger's stepfather. Hank's story proves rejuvenation is possible despite seemingly impossible odds and that we need to extend the boundary line at which a disease is considered to be irreversible. On December 19, 1999, eight years after his cardiologist declared him to be a hopeless case and terminally ill, Hank celebrated his 100th birthday.

I first met Hank when he came to my office as a patient in 1989. Hank was 89 years old at the time and had psoriasis over 40% of his body. His hands were so damaged by osteoarthritis that his fingers were frozen in a half-open position with movement so minimal he couldn't turn a doorknob. My co-worker and I tried a few approaches on him but had no success. I told Hank we were out of ideas and he stopped coming back.

In late 1991 Hank went into congestive heart failure with shortness of breath. His ankles swelled to six inches in diameter and fluids were backing up into his lungs because his heart was too weak to pump effectively. On X-ray his heart was described as being "markedly enlarged." His cardiologist speculated that his heart-muscle was damaged by a silent heart attack. Almost taken for granted were other problems of old age such as arthritis and failing memory, balance, hearing and vision. Hank also got up six times at night to urinate because of prostate enlargement. Given a case like this even the best of physicians is likely to think to himself, "So much for Hank. Next patient please."

The cardiologist gave Hank diuretics to lose fluid and increased the digitalis preparation he had been taking for years to treat an irregular heartbeat but the outlook remained grim. I obtained a copy of his 1991 hospital admission records and they are filled with words like *no code* status and *living will*, subjects never found in medical charts unless the Grim Reaper has been reported to be lurking in the hallway. Hank did not want any CPR

27

or heroic measures performed if he stopped breathing or his heart stopped. The hospital record contains a direct quote from Hank, "I only want to die once."

Rodger asked if something couldn't be done to save Hank. The cardiologist responded with something like, "Look Rodger, be reasonable. We have a very sick 90 year-old man here with a basket-full of incurable old age problems. We're not miracle workers and modern medicine can't help him. We just have to accept this." Just then a serendipitous event occurred.

According to the ultimate wisdom of the Medicare system, hospitals are paid a flat amount for every admission based upon the doctor's admitting diagnosis (the system of DRGs, or Disease Related Groups). A clerk entered the doctor's diagnosis of congestive heart failure into the system and up popped the number six, the number of days Medicare would cover for Hank whether he is in the hospital three days or eight. If the stay is shorter the hospital makes money; if longer it loses money. The effect of this policy on the timing of discharge from the hospital is clear.

On the sixth day Hank was summarily discharged from the hospital and in retrospect this saved his life. In the old days when people could afford hospitals he would have stayed in his bed, gone down hill, and made a quiet exit out the back door in a box.

Hank had lived in his own home all his 90 years. He was now unable to perform minimal chores for himself and he faced the real *fate worse than death*, entering a nursing home. Rodger could not tolerate that idea so he took his father home and assumed the duties of nurse for his final days.

Rodger had a plan because he was aware of *so-called* alternative treatments that exist outside the hallowed dogmas of modern medicine. The first night home he treated Hank with the anal heater to see if it would help his prostate problem and the old man slept through the night. This was a great start because undisturbed rest is good for heart problems.

Rodger took copies of Hank's lab tests to John Kitkowski, a biochemist in Spokane, Washington. Over many years John

28

devised a unique way to tell what is going on in a person's chemistry by analyzing the interrelationships of common blood test levels. He then makes dietary and vitamin and mineral supplement recommendations designed to improve chemical functions in the body.

For example, if his evaluation indicates more acidity (a lower Ph) in cellular fluid would improve impaired chemical functions and balance a person's chemistry John advises an increased intake of beef, pork and eggs in the diet and digestive acid supplements with meals. John told another friend of mine to eat more vegetables. A diet is selected that fits an individual's genetics and chemistry like a glove and each of us is unique in what our bodies require for healthy function. By taking this step some sense is made out of the debate between meat eaters and vegetarians who philosophically believe everyone should follow their preferences.

A major part of John's regime is supplementation with trace minerals that are given in liquid form in conjunction with multivitamins. This is an oversimplification of the agenda but sufficient for understanding its application here.

Hank is a compulsive individual who, before retirement, kept train schedules running on time so he followed John's plan without deviation. He took his vitamins and trace minerals, increased the intake of meat, pork and eggs in his diet, and cut down on starches and sugars. Rodger also made sure he took a treatment with the anal heater once a week. Never has he deviated from the instructions, even to this day.

Two months later Hank approached Rodger and said, "Rodger, look at this!" He demonstrated how he could open and close his fingers freely. He had a normal range of motion and said the hands no longer hurt when he moved them.

Gradually all of his physical degeneration problems began to go away. Of most importance, his heart became progressively stronger, fluid cleared from his lungs, and his heart shrank back to normal size! With his cardiologist's cooperation the heart drugs

29

(for the irregular heart beat) were slowly tapered down to previous levels. Hank's vision improved as did his memory and balance.

Hank's hearing improved also but at a slower pace. An audiogram performed in 1996 showed he could hear frequencies of 1KHz and 2KHz but only at 90 and 100 decibels respectively (high levels of sound). A repeat audiogram in 1998 showed he could hear those frequencies at 60 and 65 decibels respectively, a marked improvement in anyone especially a man of 98 years.

As a result of his remarkable recovery Hank once again took an interest in life. He began to follow the *Seattle Mariner's* baseball team. He completed the crossword puzzle in the local paper every morning in ten to fifteen minutes and kept up on the news and current events. He loved to watch historical documentaries on public television and read the *Smithsonian Journal*.

During the war in Yugoslavia in the 90s Hank was the only person I knew who understood what was going on. He could recite the goals and activities of the three sides, knew who was doing what to whom and understood all of the convoluted history of the area.

Hank out-lived all of his friends and his wife died in 1988. To fill this void Rodger wanted Hank to develop some social outlet, urged him to join a senior bowling league and he did. During bowling season (winter) Rodger drives Hank to the bowling alley every Monday. Although a good ten to fifteen years older than his teammates, Hank became a star of the team. He occasionally bowled a second time during the week filling in for younger 70 and 80 year olds who are dropping out due to illness or death. Some seasons he has maintained a remarkable average of 155. Other senior bowlers like to come up and touch his arm or hand in admiration and for good luck.

I have visited with Hank many times over the past eight years. He is a bit hunched over now but remains a physically strong individual. He always has a smile on his face and greets you with a strong handshake. He has a good sense of humor and likes to play practical jokes. When I told him I wanted to use his story in a book he asked me for 5% of the profits. When I asked to take his picture he turned his back to me explaining I had not clarified if I wanted a picture of his front or back. Now I wish I had taken a photo of the back of his head because his gray hair is turning back to black.

Hank remains agile for his age. During the summer months he goes outside and waters the lawn and flowers. In the fall he rakes up the leaves. One recent winter Rodger returned home to Spokane from a trip and found six inches of fresh snow on the ground. He worried about what he might find at home but there was no reason for the fear. Hank had shoveled off the 75 foot-long driveway and all the walks. These are just some of the ways he gets exercise. When he can't be active outside he walks several miles a day on a treadmill in his room, one mile at a time.

In 1998 my wife and I were parking in front of Rodger's home when we noticed Hank outside doing something in the carport. He completed his chores and headed for the stairs to return to the house. Six concrete steps lead up to a porch on the front of the home and there are no railings on the sides. Instead of coming around to the front of the steps Hank approached from the side, stepped up on the third step, and continued into the house. My wife reacted by saying, "Did you see that?" What a story of rejuvenation! Ponce de Leon would be envious.

Everything continued to go well until the summer of 1999. Hank continued to use the anal heater once a week and carefully followed his chemistry-balancing program. Then something changed. He lost interest in being active and said he didn't feel like bowling when it resumed in the fall. Rodger wasn't going to take this lying down so he began putting him through his newest collection of treatments.

Hank began to use the rectal delivery system for trace minerals and took an infrared sauna weekly. This was followed with exposure to blankets of pulsed LED lights and the anal heater. Within two weeks Hank's outlook brightened. He told Rodger there were actually two senior leagues and he wanted to sign up for both. Soon he was recording scores from 150 to 175

31

again. The week before his 100th birthday he bowled a 176 game. Two months after his 100th birthday he bowled a 192 game!

A few months prior to his 100th birthday Hank had a routine examination performed by the same cardiologist who declared him to be terminally ill in 1991. The report read: "Hank's heart is normal in size and his body resembles that of a 65 year-old man." Rodger jokingly says he plans to keep Hank alive forever just to show it's possible.

Rodger keeps Hank on a simple diet high in animal proteins and fats, whole grains and fresh foods, at least most of the time. A typical breakfast might be bacon, ham, two or three eggs, coffee and whole-wheat toast buttered with real butter. One more beautiful exception to the lousy cholesterol theory!

Hank does have a dietary vice. He polishes off about two whole pies a week. I have preached the health benefits of a low refined sugar, fresh unrefined diet for twenty-five years so I was shocked to find a collection of pies in the refrigerator.

I observed this pattern previously in China among family groups of *hard qigong masters* who perform life threatening physical stunts on stage. When I was invited for dinner in the apartment of one of these families in Beijing I found them drinking beer, chain-smoking and eating junk foods of low nutritional quality. However, they did consistently practice qigong exercises from four to six AM every day of the year regardless of weather. I these examples show that if your energy system is in balance and functioning at a high level minor, vices may be tolerated.

Winston Churchill was an example of a man with cast-iron genes for longevity. Churchill chain-smoked cigars, drank himself into a stupor every night, and lived into his 90s. However, that does not mean you and I can get away with a similar collection of bad health habits. (See color photo section for a picture of Hank)

2003 update: In the fall of 2001 Hank tripped and hit his head while watering and was admitted to the hospital for observation. In error an intern prescribed a drug for high blood pressure. Hank's pulse fell to 30 beats per minute, he had a stroke and died. So, after 100 long years, Hank was done in by an intern.

CHAPTER 4: SUCCESSFUL HEALING RESPONSES (HUMAN)

I would like to present the stories of some of the people who have been helped by this program. About ten years ago Rodger encouraged friends and neighbors to try the anal heater for a wide variety of problems just to see what might happen. The list of modalities was to grow through the decade.

A Case of Hay Fever

Rodger's neighbor to the north had lived with seasonal hay fever since he was twelve. Symptoms followed him through his life and on into retirement. At times he took anti-histaminics that caused drowsiness and occasionally he used some of the newer prescription drugs.

One spring (1991) when offending pollens appeared, Rodger suggested he use the anal heater (in a way not recommended now). Instead of using the device in the privacy of his home he decided to take the treatment while driving to Seattle. He inserted the heated probe into his anus, got into his car and began the five-hour drive. When the first battery ran down his wife changed to a second battery allowing him to take the treatment for three consecutive hours. He made certain not to speed because he could visualize what might happen to him if a state trooper stopped him and ordered him out of the car.

That night he suffered the worst hay fever episode of his life. He sneezed violently and his eyes swelled shut. The next day all symptoms cleared and he has been free of hay fever for nine years.

Comment: Rodger speculated from the rectal cancer cases in China that somehow the anal heater might strengthen the immune system. Exaggerated symptoms followed by permanent relief is sometimes reported following *natural* treatments and is referred to as a *healing crisis*. Rodger no longer recommends use of the anal heater for such long periods.

Chronic Shingles

Shingles refers to an area of blisters on the skin that are distributed over the course of a nerve, generally in the chest or abdomen. The eruption is almost always limited to one side of the body. The skin ulcerates (loses its surface) leaving raw nerve endings exposed. Pain is intense and in a small percentage of cases the skin does not heal for long periods of time, or never. In some cases the skin heals but the pain continues for a lifetime (called post-herpetic pain).

Children get chicken pox and recover but the herpes zoster virus lives on in the body in a dormant (sleeping) state. Later in life when the immune system is under increased stress (ie. death of a spouse, illness, malnutrition) many people experience a flare up of the virus in the form of shingles.

Rodger's neighbor to the south suffered an outbreak of shingles that lasted for several months. He advised her to use the anal heater and the skin eruption and pain cleared up within days.

Comment: I once had a short outbreak of shingles and can testify that the pain is intense. I can't imagine living with the problem for very long. This is but one more example of the anal heater speeding healing while stimulating the immune defenses to control a virus that continues to live on in the body.

Prostrate Enlargement (Benign Prostatic Hypertrophy, or BPH)

By far the greatest use of the anal heater outside of its use for hemorrhoids has been in cases of enlargement of the prostate. The prostate gland surrounds the urethra (urinary tube) at its outlet from the bladder. For unknown reasons it is common for the tissue of the prostate to enlarge as men get older and this squeezes down the opening of the urethra. This prevents the

34

bladder from emptying completely and soon the bladder is full again.

I have played golf many times with men who have this problem. Some go off into the woods to urinate behind a tree four or five times during a round because bathrooms on the course are too far apart for them.

Conventional treatment now offers surgical intervention and several synthetic drug products that reduce symptoms. Alternative medicine offers nutritional support for the prostate using zinc and essential fatty acid supplements as well as the herb seranoa repans (saw palmetto). The anal heater has produced much more profound results and more rapidly.

As mentioned previously the first inkling that the heater could help BPH occurred when it was being tested in clinical trials for FDA clearance around 1980. The first test subject was a man with hemorrhoids who reported that not only did his hemorrhoids shrink but he was no longer forced to get up at night several times to urinate.

I believe the next prostate patient (outside of China) was Hank whose case is described in the preceding chapter. If you skipped Chapter 3, Hank developed congestive heart failure at the age of 90 and almost died. He also was forced to get up six times at night to urinate, a stressful pattern in an old man whose ticker is failing. Rodger remembered the experiences of the farmer in the clinical trials and got Hank to try the heater. That night Hank slept all night and awoke rested.

In 1992 Rodger told me about Hank's prostate problem and his wonderful response to the heater. I began recommending the device to patients with prostate problems and continued to do so until I retired in 1996. Over those four years I can truly say the response was impressive.

Probably 80% of men with symptoms of an enlarged prostate who tried the heater slept through the first night unless they drank fluids in the evening. The result was less than perfect in a few cases and I know of only one man where it failed to help at all. The response was usually so rapid and dramatic that after supplying a patient with an anal heater I expected to receive a phone call from him the next day describing some kind of miracle.

I asked Rodger how many units have been returned throughout the history of the device. He said that only seven or eight have been returned out of the 3,000 units sold.

In 1998 the head of a pre-paid health plan tried the anal heater for his prostate symptoms (BPH) and results were swift and dramatic. Within weeks most members of the board of directors had their own units and were reporting success as well. The organization was looking for more inexpensive and less risky approaches to medical treatment and the anal heater fit right in because it could save them $15,000 for every prostate surgery avoided.

Comment: A device similar to Rodger's anal heater is available in Europe and that manufacturer is also reporting an 80% effectiveness rate in BPH. How the anal heater helps prostate problems is not clear because the tip is not long enough to reach the gland. This will be explored later in the chapter dealing with theories.

A Stubborn Case of Prostatitis

Prostatitis refers to an infection in the prostate. You would think that with modern antibiotics the infection would respond and go away, but it isn't that easy. Antibiotics have a hard time crossing from the blood into the prostate and many men suffer prostatitis problems for a lifetime.

Symptoms of prostatitis include low pelvic pain, muscle spasms in the pelvis, and frequent urination. Urologists treat flare-ups by sticking a finger into the anus and massaging the prostate, a most uncomfortable and humbling experience. It certainly lets you know who is in charge.

Tris Trethart MD of Edmonton, Alberta, reported the first dramatic case of prostatitis responding to the anal heater. Malcom W developed prostatitis at the age of 36. For a fifteen-year period he had to urinate every 40 minutes day and night. This caused severe sleep deprivation and made him feel like a zombie. He told me he was barely able to keep his job in the educational system. Relief with antibiotics was only marginal and he continued to look for a better solution.

When he was 51 Malcom stumbled across a small article describing the anal heater and he ordered one. Following instructions (in 1991) he inserted the instrument at bedtime and fell asleep with it secured in place. Following this pattern his treatments were lasting 60 to 90 minutes.

With flare-ups he used the device this way for two weeks on, one week off. Rodger also asked him to insert a frozen suppository of water in the anus before each heater treatment as a shock stimulus as described for centuries in folk healing. Malcolm says his symptoms are better suppressed when he does both.

After a short time his symptoms diminished and he was able to go for longer periods without using the instrument. He continues to use the anal heater as needed and has done so for the past nine years with good results. No cure is being claimed but he is one happy man and can once again lead a normal life.

Malcolm related that during all these years when his symptoms worsened his white blood cell count would fall to as low as 1,000 (normal is 5,000 to 10,000 per cc. blood). Now when he gets a flare-up and uses the anal heater his white count stays in the normal range. Malcolm also added he has not had a cold or flu during the past nine years (neither has Rodger) and this he attributes to the heater.

This story from Canada reminds me of an odd experience we had a few years ago. My wife and I were on our way to our cabin in British Columbia and I was taking a Thermotherapy unit to a neighbor (with its invoice). We expected Canadian border officials to charge us the customary 7% federal General Services Tax (GST).

I drove up to the window and passed the invoice to a female Customs official who was in her late twenties. The invoice clearly said *hemorrhoid machine.* She did not lift her eyes from the paper for a good half minute as her brain mulled this over. She handed the paper back to me and wished us a safe trip not wanting to delve into the subject.

Comment: Chronic prostatitis continues to be an enigma for western medicine. In 1999 a review article stated the cure rate is only about 40% with antibiotics. It is a shame researchers in this area remain unaware of results with the anal heater. Heated probes were commonly used in medicine prior to the advent of antibiotics and got lost in the shuffle even though they worked. The 1936 article describing the successful use of a heated probe to treat prostatitis is mentioned in Chapter 1 and the reference is listed in the bibliography.

A Case of Chronic Anal Fissure

Anal fissures are not exactly table talk and sufferers don't have anything to laugh about. A fissure is a fancy name for an ulcer (raw tissue with no skin covering) near the anus that refuses to heal.

In 1992 Rodger attended the annual meeting of the *Cancer Control Society* in Los Angeles. He had been selling anal heaters to a cancer clinic in Mexico for some time and was dining with the head of the clinic. Doctors south of the border were raving about how well their patients were doing when they added the anal heater to the overall regime. Rodger was enjoying the praise.

An American MD and his wife were seated at the table with Rodger and the physician worked with one of the clinics across the border. When the doctor's wife suddenly realized Rodger was the man who invented the anal heater she arose from her chair, hurried around the table and threw her arms around him. She tearfully told her story of how she had lived in pain from a fissure for twenty years and how it quickly healed after using the anal heater. Rodger had a friend for life.

Effects on Wound Healing

In 1993 Rodger was broad sided while driving and many of his teeth were knocked out. He decided to have the remainder of his teeth removed, replacing them with full upper and lower dentures. This was another opportunity to study wound healing and he used the heater for 40 minutes the night before the oral surgery. Before the extractions he had made appointments with two general dentists in order to obtain two independent opinions regarding the speed of healing on post-op day #1.

Following the extractions he was given a prescription for strong pain pills (narcotics) but found he had no need for them. He experienced little pain, almost no bleeding and no swelling.

One of the general dentists who examined Rodger is also my dentist. Bob told me when he saw Rodger the day after the full mouth extractions that his wounds looked more like the surgery was three weeks old. On a follow up visit the oral surgeon was also amazed at the speed of healing and lack of normal tissue reactions from the extractions.

A Dry Socket

Hearing this result I tried the method in a case of a *dry socket*. One of my daughter's friends had a wisdom tooth removed but no healing occurred over a two-month period (this is called a *dry socket*). During this time the raw tooth bed continued to torment her with pain so severe that she dropped out of college. Following her oral surgeon's advice she irrigated the hole and packed it with iodine soaked gauze twice a day, but no healing occurred and no additional ideas were offered. She tried the anal heater along with some vitamin/mineral supplements. The pain stopped in a few days and the raw spot was completely healed in about 10 days.

Comment: These results are amazing and obvious because they involve tissues we can observe with our eyes. It is logical to assume that the same responses must occur deeper in the body as well.

Effects on the Immune System

The anal heater appears to stimulate the immune system in a favorable way. Rodger first noticed this effect in his father who was using the heater weekly for his prostate. Hank went through the first winter of use without experiencing a cold or flu. Rodger began to use his own heater on a weekly basis to see if he could also gain protection from winter illness and they have both now have used the heater for eight years. Rodger has not experienced a flu or cold during that time. Hank has had the flu a few times during those years but each occurrence has been mild.

In the early 1990s Rodger was asked to help a woman who was receiving chemotherapy for advanced bladder cancer. Mrs. Q was in her seventies and had been the nurse who helped coordinate one of the FDA trials of the anal heater in the early 1980s. The problem was that her chemotherapy treatments kept her white count suppressed for too long. Following each treatment her white cell count fell to below 2,000 and stayed there for more than two months. Then it would rise to over 3,500 (white cells per cubic milliliter of blood) and another dose could be given.

Mrs. Q used the anal heater immediately following her next three chemotherapy sessions. Each time, to everyone's surprise, her white count rose to normal within a week. Once again this is an example of the anal heater having a favorable effect on the immune system.

Cancer of the Colon with 15 Liver Metastases

Fifty-seven year old Julius Presta is a school principal and administrator who had been well all of his life until he experienced right-sided abdominal pain in early 1999. A tumor was found in the right side of his colon that was the size of two fists held together. It was stuck to his abdominal wall and had spread to lymph nodes in the abdomen. On CAT scan there were three areas of spread (metastases) in the liver. Given the current state of treatment this is an automatic death sentence.

Jules was scheduled for abdominal surgery within days. Because of previous experiences with improved wound healing Rodger advised him to use the anal heater pre-op. Jules took forty-minute treatments on two successive days. In surgery (May 19, 1999) one-third of Jules colon was removed, the colon was hooked together without a colostomy, and lymph nodes containing cancer were removed. One of the tumors in his liver was biopsied and was positive for colon cancer. Jules' surgeon told him he had lost only two teaspoons full of blood during surgery and afterward his surgical wound healed very rapidly.

Jules and his oncologist considered chemotherapy but Jules was hesitant. In the best of cases tumors shrink for a few months, then return to grow again, and the patient goes on to die. No long-term survivors are reported after colon cancer has spread into the liver or bones.

Six weeks following surgery he was checked again. His CAT scan showed an increase in the number of liver tumors to "over fifteen" with the largest now 1.9 cm. in diameter. His CEA (a blood test for colon cancer) rose to 55.6 (normal is under 4). It was time for a difficult decision and Jules decided to try chemo.

About the same time Jules started chemo (the oral drug Xeloda) Rodger was adding one modality upon another to his healing regime. Jules added these modalities one by one eventually including the rectal minerals, a niacin flush with vitamin C and ribose, the anal heater, infrared sauna, and pulsed LED blankets. In the early months he received Reiki treatments (an energy based hands-on treatment from Japan) from John Graves, a local Reiki therapist. He used all of Rodger's modalities consistently twice a week and has continued to do so since that time. Jules has done very well and has remained free of side

41

effects from the chemo except for a brief episode in August of 1999 when the dose needed to be reduced.

Soon it was time to repeat the CAT scan. Jules came to the oncologist's office accompanied by his wife and family.

The oncologist had good news. All but one of the metastases had disappeared completely and the last one had shrunk in size! The doctors told him they had never seen this good a result in a case similar to his. Everyone, including the doctors, broke out in tears and had a good cry. One month later another CAT scan showed *all* liver tumors had vanished and his CEA test fell to a normal of 2.1.

Ten weeks later Jules was checked again. His CEA had risen and a CAT scan showed three tiny metastases in the liver. An MRI was negative for bone spread. Jules resumed the Xeloda and continued to use Rodger's regime twice a week. In April of 2000 the three new metastases were obliterated with a new treatment using microwave and ultrasound.

It is now thirteen months since the fifteen metastases in the liver were seen on the CAT scan and he continues to live a normal life free of symptoms and apparently free of cancer. How this will end is not known at present but his story is quite remarkable given the typical downhill course of this disease.

Because two treatments were used at once (chemo and Rodger's) it becomes difficult to determine exactly where the credit lies and anyone involved can legitimately claim a piece of the good result. Jules' oncologist wrote in his progress notes that this was an excellent response to orthodox chemotherapy (Xeloda) but I believe this is unlikely.

I looked up abstracts of articles describing the treatment with Xeloda in people with liver metastases from colon cancer. In the most positive studies the metastases shrink in 14% to 21% of patients, then return and grow again in a few months with no survivors. This would indicate that in 79% to 86% of patients with metastases from the colon the Xeloda has no effect at all (except for side effects).

42

I wrote to the medical director of Hoffman LaRoche Pharmaceuticals to ask if the company knows of any cases in which all liver metastases from colon cancer have cleared with Xeloda, and received no reply. Two months later I wrote a second time and again received no reply. Results with chemo in colon cancer have been so dismal that in Europe chemo has seldom been considered as a treatment option.

A Tougher Case of Colon Cancer Case with Liver Metastases

Peter was diagnosed with cancer of the rectum in January of 1997. He had surgery and chemotherapy and over the next two years pretty much held his own even though the cancer showed up in his liver. In 1999 the tumor continued to grow. In October of that year a recurrence was found near the anus that was treated with X-ray therapy and the treatment left him with permanent burns on one buttock (with ulcers) and in the anus.

By late December of 1999 he was in bad shape. One-fourth of the liver on the right side was cancerous and the tumor had spread to the left side as well. He had lost 45 pounds (30 pounds since October), had a poor appetite, slept 10 to 12 hours a day, was chronically fatigued and just lay around waiting to die.

This was Peter's condition when he first went to Rodger's home (December 28, 1999) and I happened to be there that night. He stopped the chemotherapy and decided to try Rodger's program. I didn't think Rodger would accept him as a client because he looked so close to death. Two weeks later Peter's oncologist declared him to be a chemotherapy failure and referred him to Hospice for terminal care.

One month later things were looking up. His color returned to normal and his cheeks were pink. He needed only 8 hours of sleep, his appetite returned to normal, and he was taking an interest in reading and socializing.

Peter continued to feel well for five months even though the tumor in his liver continued to grow. He gained five pounds of real body weight (not water), takes 45-minute walks, and is busy cutting weeds. All medical people acquainted with his case are amazed that he is doing so well clinically even though he appears to be losing the big battle.

This is a truly remarkable case in many ways. Peter took a severe downturn in October of 1999 and two months later looked and felt like he was terminally ill. He stopped his chemo, reversed the clinical course of his illness, and has had more than five months of an enjoyable life instead of dying.

Another observation is that he stopped his declining course and did well without using Rodger's complete program. He couldn't use the anal heater because of pain in his anus. He couldn't sit in the sauna because of radiation burns on his buttocks and couldn't lie down because his body was too long. Essentially, all he has done is take the oral nutrients and wave a hand-held LED device set on frequency E over his liver and anal areas for 20 minutes a day (40 minutes total).

Other Cancer Cases

To this date several other people with far advanced cancers have used parts of Rodger's program and all seem to have responded favorably in some way. One 72 year old woman with lymphomas on her face, eyelids, top of the head and throughout her chest and abdomen (summer of 1999) used the anal heater, a home-made infrared sauna (a converted closet) and later purchased a red light pulsed LED blanket and took the powder mix with niacin, vitamin C and d-ribose. By the spring of 2000, 95% of the tumors had disappeared.

A man in his 30s had such a wild cancer in January of 2000 the diagnosis on his biopsy was changed twice. He had three tumors in his brain and others up and down his spine when he was first diagnosed and given only two weeks to live. He took four 92-hour drips of a highly toxic chemotherapy drug and lived with the red, white, and blue pulsed LED blanket on his body most of his waking hours. Six months later he was alive, the tumors had not grown, and he was functioning normally free of pain.

A woman in her 70s has recurrent lung cancer in both lungs. Within days of starting the vitamin C, niacin, and ribose powder and use of a red LED blanket her wheezing and thick cough cleared. Soon she was again able to walk up a hill behind her home.

These responses indicate the treatment program could be highly effective in palliative efforts to prolong useful life, reduce the need for drugs, and reduce symptoms, even in the absence of outright cures.

Radiation Proctitis Following Treatment for Cancer of the Cervix

Barbara was 53 in 1995 when she was diagnosed as having stage 3.5 cancer of the cervix. The rating scale only goes up as high as stage 4 (the worst) where the cancer has spread to the pelvic walls resulting in what is called a *frozen* pelvis.

She was treated at the University of Washington Medical Center in Seattle. First she was given 50 hours of exposure to radioactive implants placed in her cervix. Then she had surgery to remove the cancer (removal of all of her female organs) and this was followed by irradiation given externally. The radiation therapy she received caused her to develop *radiation proctitis*, a condition where the walls of the rectum and lower colon are permanently injured and normal function is disrupted. The rectum can go into spasm at any time causing the sufferer to dash for a toilet before an accident occurs. Western medicine offers no effective treatment and it never goes away.

By 1996 there was no evidence of cancer in her pelvis but a lymph node swelled up in her neck and a biopsy found it contained cervical cancer tissue. This spread was treated with three doses of chemotherapy but because of side effects the planned fourth and fifth blasts of chemo were not given.

I obtained Barbara's history in October of 1999. I was happy her cancer had not returned since 1996 but felt there was no reason to include her story in this book because conventional treatment deserved almost all of the credit for her recovery. At the

45

end of my interview I told her how well people were doing with Rodger's program and suggested she may want to try the approach. I did so never dreaming the program might help a condition in which the lining of the lower bowel has been damaged permanently by radiation therapy.

Barbara began Rodger's regime and an unexpected healing occurred. After the second treatment her proctitis symptoms cleared completely and she told her many friends that Rodger worked a miracle. She has now been free of symptoms for nine months! Medicine offers no treatment for radiation proctitis making this response all the more impressive.

A Case of Quadraplegia

Kathy led a busy normal life for her first 31 years. She grew up in Anaconda, Montana, home of a huge copper mining and smelting operation. As a young girl she liked to wander the hills, pausing at springs and streams to drink. At the age of nine she began to wonder why no trees grew for miles around and the streambeds and springs were brightly colored orange and green. At twenty-one she read an article in the local newspaper reporting that all children in the area had excessive amounts of arsenic in their bodies (from the smelter operation).

As a young woman Kathy was involved in a number of very physical activities including owning and riding horses, ballet and water skiing. Something began to go wrong with her body during her pregnancy in 1980 at the age of 31. The first symptom was a "funny feeling" in her legs and over the next few years her legs became weaker.

By 1991 she was walking with a cane. By 1993 she needed to hang onto someone to walk at all. In 1994 she became wheel-chair-bound, unable to move her legs (this pattern is called a progressive ascending paralysis). During the middle 1990s she taught a computer science course at a local college. She used a collapsible auto antenna as a pointer because she sat so low in her wheel chair. All of her problems were related to her legs; her arms continued to remain strong.

Through the years she saw many physicians, but none could diagnose her condition with certainty. Multiple Sclerosis always was considered, but the ascending paralysis and lack of any remissions were not consistent with that diagnosis, nor were CAT scans and spinal taps.

In 1996 she began to have weakness in both of her arms. By 1998 she had difficulty using her pointer. Slowly she lost all functional use of her hands and arms becoming quadraplegic and totally dependant on her husband for all her needs. She continued to teach at the college but needed a student to operate her pointer. She was also writing a book on computer science using a voice-activated system

She underwent another battery of tests and this time something did show up. A walnut-sized brain tumor was found in the back of her head as well as a small plaque showing evidence of myelin sheath damage. For the first time her doctor felt comfortable diagnosing Kathy as having Multiple Sclerosis.

In March of 1999 she had brain surgery. The tumor was removed and found to be benign but apparently unusual with rapidly growing cells. For this reason she was treated with radiation to her head.

Kathy didn't want brain surgery to upset her plans so the operation was scheduled during spring break. Her fighting spirit was so great she was back in the classroom the following Monday!

Use of her arms and hands did not improve following the surgery and she was barely able to wiggle a finger or two. Over the next seven months she lost all movement in her hands and her fingers curled up in the contracted position typical of paralysis.

Throughout her ordeal she tried many approaches to relieve her condition. These included the services of a chiropractor, nutritionist, energy healer, etc. None helped and her MD stood by helplessly making notes documenting her downhill course.

In October of 1999 she sought out Rodger. After only her second treatment great advances occurred. She was able to raise her left arm (her dominant arm) over her head. Her fingers were now extended when relaxed and she could use both hands to drink from a glass for the first time in six months.

I observed her third treatment session (eight days after the first). In the infrared sauna for thirty minutes she broke into a sweat for the first time in years. While being treated with blankets of pulsed LEDs she could freely move both arms and touched the back of her head with her left hand for the first time in six months. Her formerly white and cold skin became flushed with a pink color and warm to the touch.

At the end of her session I took some photos. She was able to drink from a glass held in one hand without spilling (see color photo section).

I also observed Kathy during her fifth session. She liked lying under the blankets of LEDs because she felt they *energized* her. I took this as a clue to do a little informal experiment.

I covered the LED blanket with a wool blanket and concealed the control unit from her so she could not tell if the blanket was turned on or off. When the LEDs were illuminated she could raise her right elbow about four inches off the bed and move her fingers with better coordination. With the blanket turned off she couldn't raise her right elbow off of the bed and finger movements were poor. We did this several times switching the blanket on and off with a random pattern in front of several observers. I have never heard of anything like this in my life. The pulsed LED blanket was putting energy into her body that altered how well her nervous system functioned.

Enter Qigong Master Hu

Qigong master Hu from China entered the healing effort at this time. When Hu was twelve it was discovered he could heal with his hands. Although he doesn't talk much about his past we do know he lived in a monestary for a while and became an ordained Buddhist monk. The first person Hu treated in Spokane was Kathy.

Hu applied his own version of qigong on Kathy. Hu diagnoses blocks in the energy system by *seeing them* with a sixth sense, then draws them on stick drawings as dots. He then uses qigong to clear the *blockages* and rebalance the energy system as needed. He continues to watch the blocks as he treats and when they are gone he knows the patient will show improvement.

Hu worked on Kathy's energy blocks for over an hour with no visible change. Repeatedly he asked her to try to move her paralyzed legs. Kathy said she was sending messages but her legs didn't move. Then, in front of eight onlookers, including one of her computer class students, her left great toe moved voluntarily about two inches. A cheer broke out as if we were at a football game. Kathy had moved her feet for the first time in seven years. During the next 30 minutes movement increased until Kathy could slide each leg up to a 90-degree angle at the knee. More progress occurred over the next two days of treatment by qigong master Hu.

Comment: Kathy reminds me of a patient I saw about fifteen years ago. "Skinny" Rowland, a comical cowboy-poet, also grew up near Anaconda. Later in life the professor of neurology at the University of California Medical Center, San Francisco, diagnosed him as having ALS (Lou Gherig's disease). His case fit the textbook description so perfectly the professor videotaped him for teaching purposes. Residents and interns may still be watching Skinny stumble around with twitching muscles as over and over he is used as a perfect example of someone with ALS.

The only problem is, he never had ALS. Skinny had many exposures to lead (sand-blasting lead paint off of WW II Navy ships without a mask and working in a lead battery factory with poor ventilation) during his life and I diagnosed him as having lead poisoning that is known to mimic Lou Gherig's Disease (he spilled a large amount of lead in his urine after an intravenous EDTA chelation challenge). He improved a great deal with intravenous chelation therapy. His muscle twitching went away, he was able to give up using arm crutches, remarried (after waiting for years to die as predicted by the professor), toured the west coast in a camper with his new bride, and recited his cowboy poems at conventions.

It is likely that the ascending paralysis both Kathy and Skinny experienced was caused by toxic metals from industrial exposure. Kathy's ability to move her legs and arms after such long periods of paralysis is phenomenal.

Another Case of Paralysis

Ann, 48, was seen at the same time as Kathy. Ann had recurring pain in her left arm for a month and woke up one morning to find she could not move the arm at all. Neurological evaluation including CAT scans and MRI of her head and neck were negative and the diagnosis of MS was entertained. She had not been able to move her dominant left hand or arm for one month when qigong master Hu came to town.

Hu scanned Ann visually observing her aura, drew a *stickman* drawing and located three energy blocks on her left side in the upper abdominal area. He said each was about one-inch in diameter and looked like a black hole in a yellow-white background. He took out an atlas of anatomy and pointed to the left side of vertebrae T-12, L-1 and L-2. Hu said these energy blocks were the cause of Ann's paralysis. Independently, Sheila Berger, a local *healer* who was trying to learn from Hu, scanned Ann and drew exactly the same drawing. In western medicine such actions would be considered voodoo.

With Ann lying on her back on a treatment table qigong master Hu stepped up onto a chair so he could press down on her lower left abdomen. He pressed so hard she pleaded for him to stop, but Hu was relentless. He told her if she wanted to move her arm she would need to put up with some discomfort. He asked me to hold Ann's right hand and pump energy into it. I joked to

Left: Qigong Master Hu's Drawing of Ann's Energy Blocks

Right: Energy Blocks as Drawn by Sheila

Drawing: Tracings of Ann's energy blocks as drawn independently by qigong master Hu (left) and Sheila (right).

onlookers the real reason Hu wanted me to hold Ann's arm was to prevent her from slugging him with her arm that moved.

The abdominal pressure continued. After about 30 minutes passed Hu told us the blocks were opened and Ann could move her hand. She tried really hard and her left hand moved about an inch. By the end of the session she raised the arm about one third of the way to shoulder height and flexed her fingers. The following day after another treatment with Hu she was able to raise the arm even higher.

Hu told her if she continued to work her arm she would get better in fifteen days. Fourteen days later she began to move her thumb for the first time.

Ann has worked hard to exercise her arm and has continued to take treatments from Rodger. Now, after about five months, she has gained back about 85% of the use of her arm and hand. Hu predicted a complete recovery if she continues to do her exercises.

Because of my experiment with Kathy I tried the same with Ann. With the blanket turned on Ann could move her left arm much more freely than when it was turned off. With Ann unaware of my switching we tried this several times with the same results.

Comment: The cause of Ann's paralysis is unknown. Given her regained ability to move her arm I am certain her neurologist would say she had a psychological paralysis. The interesting thing is the first movement in her arm occurred while being treated by qigong master Hu and he told us in advance exactly when it was going to occur. Because she had been paralyzed for 30 days the odds against her beginning to move her arm spontaneously at that exact minute would be about 43,000 to 1. Actually, since her doctors didn't expect her to regain movement at all, they would be higher than that.

Allergic to the Twentieth Century

Between 1976 and 1990 most of my practice was devoted to what is now called *environmental medicine*, a bastard stepchild of the field of allergy. Some of the most difficult patients in this arena are sensitive to almost everything, such as inhalants, chemical fumes, foods, medicines and even their homes. You name it; they are sensitive to it.

Mary lived a normal life until around 1983 when she became ill at age 36. Her home was built over an underground spring and she developed an allergy to molds in her damp basement. Soon, her sensitivities spread to chemical fumes including gasoline, gas heat, newsprint, formaldehyde, perfumes, paints and cosmetics. When she wore polyester she felt like raw nerves were sticking out of her skin. Her chemical and mold problems became so bad she was forced to live outside of her home.

She found she could tolerate cotton and had to find non-petrochemical-based materials for clothing, bedding and household items. As the problem progressed she became sensitive to almost every food. Eventually she could tolerate little more than rice.

In 1994 she tried John Kitkowski's biochemistry balancing program. She says this helped with many of the food sensitivities and some of the chemical sensitivities, but she still had a bad problem with molds and most chemicals and fit the typical picture of a chemically sensitive person.

In 1995 friends referred her to Rodger for a part time job cleaning his home. When she first went to his home she was so sensitive to the fumes she did could not enter. Rodger made one room on the back of his home chemically free so she could come inside and not become ill. He did reflexology on her feet and began to add additional treatments as time went by.

Gradually, Mary's sensitivities diminished. At present (2000) she still has problems with molds. Foods are not a problem and she reacts only to strong chemical fumes such as gasoline, pesticides, etc. Mary feels the pulsed LEDs and saunas helped her the most of the various modalities in the regime. She tolerates being inside Rodger's home and frequently cleans for him as a way to return the favor. More recently, she has gotten over almost all of her sensitivities, returned to school full time and is getting straight As, a feat she never would have dreamed possible.

Comment: Becoming sensitive to the chemical environment is one of the worst things you could wish on anyone. Theron Randolph MD of Chicago documented the first case of sensitivity to the chemical environment in 1951. Ted took long detailed patient histories and typed every word of the questions and answers. One day, when nobody came to his office because of an ice storm, he used the time to do some detective work on one of his worst treatment failures.

The patient was a doctor's wife from Michigan who developed lightheadedness, confusion, stuffy nose and rashes when exposed to common materials such as perfumes, cosmetics, lipstick, deodorant, smog, auto exhaust and smoke stack fumes from the steel plants in Gary, Indiana. When she avoided these exposures she remained perfectly well.

Several years ago I had the opportunity to spend the night as the guest of Ted and his wife Trudy in their apartment high above the smog of Chicago. Ted took out the chart of that first patient and showed me how he used a red pencil to underline all the symptoms she was able to connect with exposures to specific things. When he looked for a common thread all of the symptom-triggering materials were related to man-made chemical materials or their combustion products. It was a tale worthy of Sherlock Holmes.

Complete recoveries in people with chemical sensitivities are rare. Most are forced to go through life with their guard up, occasionally being hit by surprise with some apparently innocent exposure that throws them out of control but does not affect others. One patient of mine told me such a story.

This woman worked as a checker at a variety store. She was well aware that perfume fumes caused her to have an attack of asthma. One morning a perfume-dowsed customer was second in line at the check out counter and the excessive amount of fumes started her wheezing. When the woman was immediately adjacent to her the wheezing became far worse and obvious to all around. At that point the customer offered the checker some advice saying, "You know, Honey, you really should do something about that wheezing."

Weight Reduction and Aches and Pains

Laura Lamoreux of Anchorage, Alaska, runs a most unusual weight loss business that incorporates some of the modalities of Rodger's regime. The path to her current avocation began when she was almost killed in 1993 when a truck crashed into her car.

54

The accident injured neck bones from C-2 through C-6, crushing discs and nearly severing her spinal cord. Following surgery she found she had lost most of the use of her hands and she dragged her feet when walking. In 1996 she received medical care at the Cleveland Clinic Foundation Center for the Spine and fashioned her recovery from information she acquired there and in post-graduate physical therapy courses.

Through a process of self-education in nutrition, graduate level courses, physical therapy and many other disciplines, Laura fashioned a program for herself and recovered about 99% (She says her head still *twitches* when she is angry). It also helped that Laura was a natural healer. She remembers *making everything better* as a toddler. Her abilities were obvious to her stepmother who actively encouraged her to try to heal others when she was thirteen. Her efforts to *heal with the hands* led to a string of success stories involving pets and neighbors.

When she returned to Anchorage two of her physicians discovered how well she was doing and began to refer patients to her hoping she could help them. The first referrals were people with injuries similar to hers. She was so successful that more and more people came and the volume of patients grew by word of mouth until in 1996 she was forced to move to a business location.

In the fall of 1998 she heard about Rodger's activities. In early 1999 she added the infrared sauna, the anal heater, and a body wrap to her list of methods. She also encourages clients to eat the highest quality foods (whole grains, cheese, liver, fish, pork, butter, oils containing essential fatty acids and supplements with trace minerals and electrolytes).

Laura found people were more likely to recover when they improved their nutritional status. Overweight people lost weight and she became a believer in the theory that many people over-eat because their bodies are trying to get the quantities of essential nutrients they need from low nutrient density foods. Her business grew to where now she is open 40 hours a week and was recently forced to add her seventh sauna.

55

Laura's business card lists her activities as *figure shaping* and *pain reduction.* However, when she applies the range of modalities to people with these and other problems (which includes most people) she gets feedback about other conditions that improve as well. Some of these anecdotal reports are listed below:

1. One elderly man had a stroke in 1984 that left him paralyzed in one arm and leg. He called Laura to complain he was recovering so much use in his arm and leg he was thrashing about in his sleep and he didn't like this.

2. Many women with chronic vaginal yeast infections report they no longer have recurrences.

3. A lady who had a hip replacement ten years previously had so much pain in the other hip that normal activity was impaired and another surgery appeared to be needed. She used trace minerals, the infrared sauna, qigong machine, calcium supplements and MSM, an oral sulfur supplement. After a few sessions she felt so well she stopped thinking about surgery and took a vacation in Florida.

4. One woman had head and neck pains for twelve years. She worked down the street running the biofeedback equipment at a local physical therapy office. While using the whole package of modalities all symptoms cleared. The client then volunteered that at the physical therapy office where she worked she seldom saw any people with similar problems get better.

5. A man with cancer of the prostate took the trace minerals, saunas, several herbs and tried the anal heater, but only for a few treatments because of esthetics. His cancer disappeared.

6. A 30 year-old woman with endometriosis used the trace minerals and took the sauna for 30 minutes holding the LED blanket over her painful abdomen for ten minutes. By the next day the acute pain had subsided. She began using the anal heater along with the other modalities. Within five days she had little discomfort and her skin looked *radiant.* In the next

month she lost eight pounds and has had no more pelvic pains.

Comment: These cases are excellent examples of how these modalities can benefit people. They also show the modalities can work far from Rodger and his personal qigong energy field. Laura's case reports are not confirmed nor carefully studied as she is not in the business of providing health care and makes no claims in that area. Possibly others will copy her lead and set up facilities equipped with similar devices in other cities.

More on Weight Loss

As long as the subject of weight loss has come up now is a good time to mention Rodger's own experience. When I met Rodger in 1981 he was five feet five inches tall and weighed 188 pounds. He was bald, had a large rounded abdomen and looked like he was stuffed into his clothes. Everyone called him the *Little Buddha*. Those days are gone.

Rodger began to use all modalities in his program in mid 1999. Over a period of four months he lost 35 pounds and now is an almost svelte 153 pounds. This unexpected circumstance caused him to search trunks in his attic for clothes that fitted him forty years ago. He says he makes no effort to count calories or to lose weight. He just doesn't feel like overeating any more.

A Little Theory About Weight Loss

This type of weight change is compatible with the theories of Traditional Chinese Medicine. TCM theories state that if a person can bring the energy system into a state of balance and harmony the body will self-correct itself toward normal. Underweight people will gain weight to optimal levels and overweight people will lose weight to optimal levels.

Americans spend billions of dollars every year on diets, books, programs, prepackaged foods, pills, herbs, fat *burners,* fat blockers, stomach stapling, intestinal bypasses and many other wild ideas, all in an effort to lose weight. Most weight loss efforts attack the problem from a single limited approach and fail, never coming close to balancing body energies as required.

CHAPTER 5: SUCCESSFUL HEALING RESPONSES (ANIMAL)

Alternative and complementary medicine principles apply to animals as well as humans. An 800-page book on the subject in veterinary medicine was published in 1998. Major sections of the book cover subjects such as acupuncture, chiropractic treatment, massage therapy, Traditional Chinese Medicine, herbal medicine, homeopathy, nutrition, Ayurvedic medicine (from India) and low energy photon therapy (use of LLLT and LEDs). An acupuncture supply company in Canada sells individual books on homeopathic treatment of different animals such as the goat, pig and bird.

Therefore, it should come as no surprise to learn that some of the modalities in the program described in this book are being used successfully in animals. In fact, there is almost a 20-year history of the use of pulsed LEDs on animals.

Animal Users of the Anal Heater

We believe the first canine to use an anal heater was Panda, Rodger's old dog. Panda was a small dog that lived to the ripe old age of seventeen or 119 in human years (experiences with Panda and Hank prove longevity is common in Rodger's family). I knew the dog as an irritable little snip, an unpredictable bother that frequently tried to bite my fingers when I tried to pet her. Who else but Rodger would expect a miracle just because he stuck a heated probe into an old dog's anus?

In 1995 Panda became quite ill, sleeping all the time and too tired to go outside when she should. Rodger took her to a vet who checked her, drew blood and had the lab run it right away because of her poor condition. The BUN was 302 mg/dl and the creatinine 4.7 mg/dl, both indicating kidney failure (the name on the lab report was *canine Panda Estes*). When the results came back the vet said to Rodger, "This dog is as good as dead. Panda is in end stage kidney failure and the only humane thing to do is to put her to sleep right now." If you remove the pitch for euthanasia this sounds like what happened to Hank.

Once again Rodger had other plans. He took Panda back home, placed her across his lap, and gave her a 30-minute treatment with the anal heater. The next morning Panda was walking about normally, eating well, and once again asking to go outside when appropriate. Rodger took Panda back to the vet two days later to repeat the blood work. The BUN had fallen to 85.4 mg/dl, still elevated (normal is 7 to 28 mg/dl), but low enough to function normally. Panda led a normal enjoyable life for the next two weeks before dying peacefully of old age in her sleep.

Adding two weeks to a mean old dog's life may not seem worthwhile but the veterinarian said she was as good as dead when he first saw her. This is the only time we know of where the anal heater has been used to treat kidney failure. My old acupuncture book recommends stimulation of energy point Conception Vessel #1 (near the anus) to treat anuria (no production of urine, the same thing as kidney failure). Chinese Medicine five element theories also say that metal controls water, therefore the aluminum heater probe controls kidney function.

Scamper

Rodger's current dog, Scamper, reminds me a lot of Panda. She is small, old, feisty and demanding. In 1999 she was turning gray and her hair was dry, resembling that of teenage girls who foul up their fatty acid balance by eating French fries and other deep-fried fast foods containing *trans*-fats.

As Rodger developed his program he noticed Scamper wanted to participate. When someone was lying down with blankets of LEDs covering the body Scamper insisted on being lifted on to the bed where she curled up under the lights. Long after the client had finished and left the scene Scamper could be found sleeping under the blankets. Rodger also gave her periodic treatments with the anal heater, using the dog's personal probe, and added trace minerals to her drinking water.

Six months later a marked improvement could be seen. Scamper lost all of her gray hairs and her coat became shinny and lustrous similar to coats of dogs in pet food commercials. I should add at this time that Rodger, Hank and I all have seen many of our gray hairs turn back to black or brown on this program.

A Horse With Hives

In 1995 Rodger received a call from a friend deeply involved in the horse business. A two-year old gelding named *Pinky*, recently purchased for $8,000, had a bad case of hives all over his body. The hives suddenly popped up four weeks previously and never cleared. Pinky spent the day rubbing up against anything he could find and his appetite was poor.

A vet checked the horse for the usual causes of hives and came up blank. This outcome is expected in similar cases in humans as well where a cause of hives is found in only 10% of cases. The only course of action appeared to be to pull out the needle and syringe and smother Pinky's symptoms with high doses of cortisone for whatever time was needed, probably the rest of his life. Pinky's cash value was sinking daily when the anal heater man came to the rescue.

Rodger's inventive mind whirled into action once more. He was trying the anal heater on everything at the time so why not on this horse? He observed how anal heat improved immune function in other situations but the big problem was that a human-sized heater would not be up to the job at hand. Rodger's mechanically minded son was assigned the task and three days later Rodger headed thirty miles out to the stable with a twelve-inch long anal heater made out of one inch diameter aluminum.

With poor Pinky restrained by a twitch (a painful restraint on the upper lip) Rodger held the heater in the horse's anus for forty minutes (he remembers very well because the anus was at eye level). This creates a funny visual image if you have a creative

61

mind but the end of the story is that the treatment worked. The very next day Pinky was free of hives, eating everything in sight, and running with a vigorous stride. The hives never returned. (Please see photo in color photo section.)

Comment: Allergists hate to see cases of chronic giant hives (chronic urticaria) come in the door because a cause of the reaction is seldom found. It should come as no surprise that animals suffer most of the same ills as humans and treatments are similar as well. This response in Pinky was outstanding, and the case also created a good photo opportunity.

I believe the success seen in this case can be explained through the theories of Chinese Medicine. When I told this story to Dan Parris he immediately commented, "Boy, they sure gave the Governing Vessel meridian a good crank from both ends, didn't they?" What he meant by this was that both ends of the Governing Vessel meridian were being stimulated at the same time, GV #27 on the upper lip with the twitch and GV #1 near the anus with the heater.

Effects on Wound Healing

Dan Parris shared several photographs of amazing healing in horses with the use of pulsed LEDs. First there was a horse named *Dude* that got a leg tangled in barbed wire, pulled free but in doing so tore off an area of skin (full thickness) about four by six inches. During the next five weeks the wound was cleaned and kept covered under the supervision of a veterinarian, but no healing occurred.

Then a trainer began to use a pad of infrared LEDs pulsed at Nogier's frequency A (for skin or ectoderm) twice a day for fifteen minutes. No other treatments were involved at this point except to keep the wound clean.

Healing occurred at a remarkable rate. In fifteen days new skin grew in to cover the entire wound and this new skin was covered with hair except in one small area. All of the area was covered by hair in an additional ten days. (Photos in photo section)

In another incident a mare and her colt returned home with injuries apparently caused by running into barbed wire. The wounds were dirty and appeared to be about two days old. The mare had a gaping wound above the front legs where skin was torn off of an area about 16 by 8 inches with underlying muscles exposed.

The open area was cleansed and washed with a solution of honey, insulin and DSMO found by veterinarian acupuncturists to speed healing. Then it was treated with two hand held pointed instruments, one an LED, the other a cold laser, both pulsed at Nogier's frequency A for skin (ectoderm). These instruments were used (1986) because the veterinarian's infrared LED pads were on loan at the time. 45 days later the wound was completely healed. (see photo section)

The colt was about four feet tall at the time. Skin was torn from the base of the neck as well as the left upper foreleg across to the midline. These injuries were treated in a similar manner and healed almost completely in four weeks and this is quite remarkable considering their extent. (see photo section)

From a medical standpoint these injuries healed cleanly and quickly. It would have been poor medicine to try to clean and cover these wounds with skin grafts in the early stages of healing. Generally when treating dirty wounds the best course of action is to let the wounds heal in from the edges by themselves.

A Rock in the Hoof

Sometimes a horse will go lame for no apparent reason. In some cases the horse has stepped on a sharp pebble that has become imbedded in its hoof. A search for a cause may come up empty. The little rock then may work itself up through the hoof and exit several inches higher at the top of the hoof. A small bubble appears that opens up and the rock passes out, but the process generally takes up to a year.

I have heard of cases where a horse has gone lame because of a rock in its hoof. When pulsed LED pads were used the process speeded up with the rocks exiting at the top of the hoof in about a month.

CHAPTER 6: HEALING METHODS IN THE PROGRAM

The modalities used in this healing program are simple, safe, available and user friendly. We are well aware of the thousands of vitamins, minerals, potions, practices, exercises, systems, herbs and other materials people try. While recognizing the existence of other worthwhile treatment methods, Rodger independently relied on his ability to sense energy vibrations with his own body. This process led him to select a very small number he found to be superior. When he began to apply these methods in combination synergistic responses occurred and this was the big surprise. Why this synergism occurs remains a mystery.

Trace minerals, an unfamiliar five-carbon sugar compound, an infrared sauna, pulsed LEDs and anal heat sounds more like a review of high school physics than a healing program. To someone unfamiliar with how well Rodger's clients have done a leap of faith is required. However, I have confidence the program will have no difficulty proving itself for the best of reasons. It works!

The biggest problem may be taking the time to apply the methods, pausing from other activities to do something good for you. In the final analysis doesn't it sound like a wonderful thing to have access to items you can use in the privacy of your own home that not only can relieve many common minor problems (such as a first aid kit) but also have the capability to prevent and cure serious diseases as well?

I would like to go through the various modalities currently in the program providing enough discussion to satisfy most people.

Trace Minerals and other Nutrients

We have observed that a healing response is more difficult or impossible to achieve if the body is poorly nourished.

Unfortunately, this description fits most Americans. Certainly all of the 50+ essential nutrients are important for normal chemical function in our tissues, but Rodger and I believe deficiencies of trace minerals deserve our attention more than other areas.

Nutrition experts agree that less is known about trace minerals than any other area in nutrition. USDA tables show refining of grains and food processing remove substantial percentages of trace minerals compared to levels found in whole grains and fresh foods. On top of that there is incomplete knowledge of how minerals are absorbed from the small intestine into the blood. It is known that each mineral is involved in a complicated mechanism that may or may not be working well. Therefore, when we take oral supplements of trace minerals we have no way to know how well they are being absorbed or whether normal cell levels are being maintained. For this reason it is best to take trace minerals in liquid or powder form (in juice or capsules) rather than in the pill form.

Rodger dreamed up the rectal administration of trace minerals in liquid form to get around the absorption question and he strongly believes this is an important component in this healing program. My own belief (unproven) is that the sicker a person is the more likely trace mineral absorption mechanisms (in the small intestine) will be malfunctioning. Therefore, really sick people should be certain to use this delivery method if they are going to give the program a chance to work.

Early in the development of the program Rodger added liquid trace minerals to distilled water, poured this mix into elongated balloons and froze them. He had clients cut off the tip of the balloon and insert the frozen finger sized object through the anus.

In practical application there are many people who find it is impossible to pass a frozen *pop sickle* through the anus as well as others who find this delivery system unacceptable. For those individuals liquid trace minerals can be given under the tongue. One goal of the program was to make available a trace mineral mix that could be given either rectally or under the tongue. Details on availability and application of such a mix of trace minerals can be found in Appendix I.

Following the trace minerals Rodger's clients drink a mixture of vitamin C (ascorbic acid), the niacin form of vitamin B-3, and d-ribose, a 5-carbon sugar. The niacin form of vitamin B-3 is used to produce a *niacin flush* that lasts for about 30 minutes. The niacin flush is intended to deliver nutrients to parts of the body that may not have the best circulation.

d-ribose is an interesting sugar compound that contains five carbon molecules. Most common sugars contain six carbon molecules. Our pathologist consultant, who once owned a string of medical diagnostic laboratories, tells us laboratories use d-ribose to stabilize DNA. If you look at the structure of DNA you will see many of the compounds that hold the two strands of DNA (the double helix) together are derivatives of ribose.

In sports medicine d-ribose is used to speed the recovery of ATP levels back to normal following heavy exertion. ATP is referred to in biochemistry as the *active* form of energy (chemical) in our cells.

For more details on how to use these materials see Appendix I. You should wait for at least one half hour following the end of the niacin flush before proceeding to the next step to prevent dehydration and a possible drop in blood pressure.

Infrared Saunas

Having access to an infrared sauna is the most difficult logistical problem in the program. Omission of the sauna certainly would cut costs and problems in carrying out the program. Even with the newly designed blanket with red, white and blue LEDs we still advise you take dry heat saunas if possible. Therefore, if a sauna is available take a 30-minute infrared sauna but wait at least one hour after the niacin flush comes to an end.

Radiant heat warms objects directly without heating intervening air. Most of the energy the sun gives off is in the form of radiant heat or infrared waves. When we feel the direct heat of the sun we are being warmed by infrared energy. For many years infrared bulbs have been installed in the ceilings of bathrooms to take the chill off after a shower on a cold morning. Therefore, we are no strangers to the infrared spectrum.

The question is, "Can infrared energy have a healing or normalizing effect on the body?" The answer appears to be yes. Medical practitioners in Japan have been advising infrared saunas for patients since 1979 and the idea is so popular over 700,000 units have been sold in that country alone.

Infrared energies penetrate a long way into the body, about an inch and a half. Ordinary heat from bath water or a hot tub penetrates only one-fourth of one inch. This deep heating effect is achievable in an infrared sauna without the air temperature rising to the uncomfortable and smothering levels created in a humid steam sauna or Indian sweat lodge.

Japanese researchers have reported beneficial results in a long list of conditions, mostly related to body aches and pains. The infrared sauna has been reported to be helpful in arthritis, low back pain and muscle spasms. It has also been reported to help menopausal symptoms, insomnia, acne and varicose veins. The list goes on and on. Perhaps one of the most dramatic results is in weight loss. Each 30-minute sauna produces enough cardiac conditioning to burn over 900 calories as you just sit there. It is no wonder stories of weight loss are being reported with the use of infrared saunas.

Infrared saunas are available in the United States but are quite expensive. Rodger purchased his in kit form from a supplier after bargaining the price down to $3,000. His sauna can seat up to three people at a time, has a temperature control, timer and built in radio and tape deck. The outside and inside are constructed of an attractive high quality cedar.

I built my sauna following Rodger's design and dimensions. Mine is constructed with wood scraps, smooth plywood on the inside, and a cedar seat. It has a timer, interior light and three 500-watt infrared heaters. Even with these cost cutting steps it still cost over $600 and looks ugly.

Rodger is currently designing an inexpensive portable infrared sauna based around a cot with infrared lamps underneath on the floor. This should be available in a kit form (in a duffle bag?) in the near future.

For precautions in the use of a sauna please see Appendix I.

Therapy with Pulsed LEDs (light emitting diodes)

After reestablishing a normal state of hydration following the sauna Rodger's clients lie under blankets containing rows of LEDs. The blankets used in this regime are but one of many delivery systems in what is called *photon therapy, light therapy,* or *phototherapy.* When Rodger is busy treating a client he is likely to cover the person with several blankets of LEDs, then wave a hand held LED device over the body directing the light through the blanket and clothing.

It is widely accepted in Europe that red LEDs have a normalizing effect on the body. These LEDs are being applied in many ways for a variety of conditions. In this country they are available in devices containing a single LED, clusters of LEDs and as small blankets containing many LEDs in a field.

As mentioned elsewhere, veterinarian Marvin Cain began to study with Paul Nogier MD of France in the late 1970s and learned of the pattern of resonance frequencies of tissues based on embryologic origin. Cain told his friend Dan Parris (of Oklahoma) about Nogier's discovery and Dan began to manufacture pulsed LED devices.

Dan aimed his products at the animal market and they have been available to animal owners, the general public and veterinarians for almost 20 years. Several companies also sell LED products for animals and humans, available as hand held devices, pads, blankets, leg straps and devices for the hoof and head.

Horse-people swear by the products. Owners of race horses and show horses are always on the prowl for new things that may give their horses an edge in competition. Response from the horse community has been good and the number of veterinarians taking an interest in acupuncture and pulsed LEDs is growing rapidly.

An extensive literature exists on therapeutic effects of light therapy and some examples are presented in Chapter 2 and Appendix III.

The Anal Heater

Rodger advises people to use an LED blanket for 15-minutes, then take a 15-minute treatment with the anal heater.

The current version of the anal heater consists of a plastic box the size of a large book containing a transformer for charging the battery plus a connecting cord that leads to an aluminum-heating probe. The unit is charged with a transformer (115 volts) that plugs into a wall outlet. The cord of the anal heater plugs into the same port on the machine as the charger. This safety feature makes it impossible to use the unit while it is plugged into house current. The anal heater will raise core body temperature of most people by about 1 degree F. in 15 minutes.

In Chinese Medicine the anus is located between the beginning energy points of two meridians that run up the front and back of the body. This is also the general location of Chakra #1 in the traditional medicine system of India. Qigong masters tell us heat stimulation in the anus provides a powerful stimulus to these energy areas as well as distant locations. The meridian system and its interlocking connections provide us with the best explanation for why the anal heater has healing effects far removed from the anus.

This completes the list of modalities Rodger has been using. The list is short, the modalities are simple in application, but the results we have been observing have been outstanding as described throughout this book

CHAPTER 7: ENERGY TREK

Body energies are difficult to measure. They are vague and mysterious to most people. Therefore it should come as no surprise to learn that many diagnostic and healing systems have evolved as individuals in different cultures began to discover and explore what can be done with these energies. Much of this material has a biographical tone because I have been fortunate to meet and study with many pioneers in this area.

Homeopathy

Samuel Hahnemann MD developed homeopathy in Germany around 1795. He served as a translator between German and British professors who were debating how drugs worked (herbs) and was intrigued by the subject. As an experiment he took full strength doses of quinine normally used to treat malaria and experienced all the symptoms of malaria. From this experience he developed the concept that symptoms of an illness are an expression of the body's efforts at fighting the illness. Therefore, it might be beneficial to give sick people materials that produce the same symptoms when they are well.

In what is said to be the first effort at a scientific drug trial he gave a group of healthy volunteers full strength doses of a compound every day for a month and asked them to record any new symptoms they experienced. From these records he collected the most commonly experienced symptoms and developed what he called a *picture* of that compound. Through exhausting work he developed a *picture* for about 30 compounds.

Later when a patient entered his clinic with a list of symptoms that closely matched the *picture* of a studied compound, he treated them with tiny dilutions of that material. Treatment results were good much of the time and it was not uncommon for some people to experience complete cures. He occasionally observed what homeopaths call *retracing* in which symptoms of all illnesses experienced in a lifetime come and go quickly in reverse order as if a computer memory disc is being run backwards.

Hahnemann discovered the more he diluted the materials (in water) the more powerful their effects became, just the opposite of logic. He used a one to ten dilution system and after every two dilutions he held the material in a test tube and pounded it on a pad (a process called succession).

After twelve such dilutions scientists tell us there will be no more molecules of the original compound in the water, but Hahnemann's most effective remedies were diluted much further, sometimes hundreds or thousands of times. This caused the medical community to attack the basic premises of homeopathy and call it *Hahnemann's nothingness.* This attitude prevails today even though many double blind studies report homeopathic treatment can work (many studies are from England).

Homeopathy arrived in the States in the early 1800s. Even if it were nothing more than a placebo, it would have become popular for the rather obvious reason it wasn't killing anyone outright. Remember, standard treatments of the era involved extensive bloodletting and poisoning the patient with mercury or other poisons to drive out the illness.

But homeopathy did work and its practitioners found they could hang out their shingle in a new town and quickly build a large and prosperous practice. This further infuriated orthodox physicians (the bloodletters), who generally were not doing well financially.

Another aspect to the problem was that the homeopaths at the time were physicians who received conventional training as well as training in homeopathy. It seems to be a pattern in human behavior that when people bolt from a dogma (reject the standard party line) they are singled out for harsher treatment than those who never followed the dogma at all. This was seen in the Spanish Inquisition where Jews who became converts to Christianity (los converses) and were suspected to be leaning back to Judaism were persecuted while Jews who never converted to Christianity were not. A more recent example is the harsh treatment of physicians practicing alternative and complementary medicine by state licensing boards simply because they are doing things differently.

Homeopathy was on the move and growing, and by 1900 there were seventeen medical schools teaching the method along with the usual medical courses. These included the former Hahnemann Medical College and the University of Michigan Medical School.

The American Medical Association was formed in 1847 and one of its first acts was to bar members from even talking with physicians who used homeopathy in their practices. At the turn of the century conventional medicine's goal was to destroy homeopathy completely while attempting to upgrade the poor quality of the majority of the country's 600 plus medical schools.

One of the concepts of homeopathy is *like heals like*. Vaccinations and allergy extract treatments grew out of homeopathy but most physicians are unaware of this as they continue to criticize the source of these accepted treatments. Vaccines and allergy extracts are made from the same materials that cause a disease or allergy.

For years homeopathy has remained popular, especially in Europe and India. In many pharmacies in Europe pharmaceutical company products are displayed on one side of the store, homeopathic remedies, herbs, vitamins and minerals on the other. American pharmacies are beginning to follow the same path.

While orthodox medicine continues to ridicule homeopathy theoretical physicists are having fun trying to explain how it works. They have no problem postulating that some kind of energetic memory can be retained in water. After all, aren't we taught in physics that everything is energy and that matter is simply energy frozen in time?

Homeopathy has also become a popular treatment method among veterinarians who practice alternative medicine. In the 1998 book, *Complementary and Alternative Veterinary Medicine*, over 60 pages are devoted to the treatment of animals with homeopathy and the catalogue for an acupuncture supply company in Canada lists books on homeopathic treatment of specific animals such as the goat, dog, bird and pig.

Acupuncture and Traditional Chinese Medicine

Prior to 1972 few Americans had heard of acupuncture. Acupuncture began to be practiced in China 4,000 to 5,000 years ago and became popular in Europe about 300 years ago. For unknown reasons it did not easily cross either ocean to the United States. In 1972 Chairman Mao decided China had been isolated from the world long enough and initiated the contact with President Nixon.

Nixon and a battery of newspaper reporters went to China. James Reston, a reporter for the *New York Times*, had his appendix removed in China in the usual way and was treated with acupuncture for post-op pain. He wrote how effective this mysterious acupuncture was and soon the word was on everyone's lips in America.

Hugh Wang MD was a colleague of mine who learned acupuncture in the early 1960s while in the US Navy. His ship spent most of his two-year enlistment anchored in Hong Kong harbor. Hugh was bored to death and knew he was getting rusty taking care of healthy young seamen.

He went to a local British hospital and asked the administrator if he could make rounds with the doctors to stay up to date. Hugh was surprised when the administrator asked him if he would like to make rounds with western-trained doctors or Traditional Chinese Medicine doctors. Each service had a wing in the hospital and both were held in equally high regard. Never having encountered a different medical system Hugh opted to learn the old ways.

Hugh was born in Shanghai but, like so many modern Chinese, knew nothing of the old medicine. The Traditional Chinese Medicine doctors taught Hugh acupuncture, but upon his return to the United States he *hung up his needles* for fear of

74

being criticized by other doctors for doing something so different in his practice. After the Nixon trip he began using acupuncture openly on his patients.

One day Hugh asked if I wanted to watch a patient deliver a baby with the use of acupuncture for pain control. The late stages of labor went smoothly for this mother-to-be but at the final moment she pushed too hard, suffering an extensive tear through the anal sphincter and three inches up the rectum. These tears generally require large amounts of local anesthetic and this one would be a good test of Hugh's abilities with the acupuncture needles.

Without hesitation Hugh sewed up the repair as if the tissues were full of Novocain. As the only board certified obstetrician in the room, I was impressed. Normally when an anal muscle is torn the muscle seems to experience a precognition of what is in store and pulls away to hide. Each torn end of the muscle forms an indentation into which the doctor must plunge a sharp-toothed clamp to pull out something solid enough to sew.

Shortly after this experience the Wongs and McGees took a vacation junket to Hong Kong. We spent nine days following Hugh as he went from one Chinese medicine shop to the next looking for acupuncture supplies from Mainland China. At meals he told stories about how people can become well through the use of Traditional Chinese Medicine, even after the western system has declared them to be hopeless.

When I returned home a brochure was waiting announcing the first acupuncture course in the United States for physicians. I took the three-day course in nearby Monterey and returned home bewildered. During lectures skepticism was written all over my face. One instructor picked me out of 200 attendees saying, "Ah, we have a *smirker* in the front row." Well, what did he expect? He just told us everything in the world is composed of the five elements; fire, wood, water, air and dirt, and I wanted nothing to do with such a silly concept.

A week later a yellow jacket stung my palm and this terrified me. I almost died from a severe allergic reaction to a fire ant bite in New Orleans a few years earlier and I was aware people who are allergic to one venom may react to other venoms. I walked slowly into the house and sat down as my thumb, index and middle finger swelled to the size of large sausages. The skin flushed red and pain shot through that part of my hand with every heartbeat.

The reaction stabilized in 30 minutes and did not spread. However, I knew the swelling could last for days and contemplated canceling two hysterectomies scheduled for the next morning. What could I do? For lack of anything better why not try acupuncture, though I knew little or nothing about its practice.

I got out my only acupuncture book and energy maps of the body and tried to find a treatment plan. The closest thing I could find was a listing in the index for *hand* that guided me to a list of six energy points. I placed needles in two points and nothing happened! What else could I do?

At the meeting I had ordered a battery powered acupuncture stimulator instrument and my wife told me it arrived that morning. We opened it up, read the directions, put in batteries, attached wire leads to the two needles with clips, and turned the intensity all the way down. Hoping for a little relief of the pain I timidly I pushed the *on* button.

What happened changed my life. All the red skin on my fingers and palm turned white instantly as if an electric switch was thrown. Soon the pain was leaving and the swelling going down. Thirty minutes later all evidence of the sting was gone.

My entire medical belief system came tumbling down. Up to this time American physicians visiting China wrote medical journal articles about acupuncture but they were all specialists in anesthesiology. Medicine was beginning to acknowledge that acupuncture may have a role in pain relief and analgesia (pain relief while awake) but other uses were dismissed as hog wash.

A giant light bulb lit up in my brain. If that was all conventional medicine knew about acupuncture as it glibly issued negative opinions on the subject, perhaps it didn't know very much about the other treatment modalities it routinely attacked in journals and the media. For me it was an awakening.

I began attending acupuncture courses and meetings all over the country. At one meeting I shared my insect sting story with practitioners far more experienced than I. The reaction I got was a "Ho hum. What is so remarkable about that?" To some my little miracle was commonplace.

In Traditional Chinese Medicine theory a vital energy named qi (also spelled chi, pronounced chee and called prana in India and ki [kee] in Japan) is the life force in our bodies. Qi originates from our breath, food and environment, even from outer space. It passes through the body through meridians or channels that exist as energy tracts that have no relationship to anatomical structures. There are twelve meridians on each side of the body and two others pass up the midline of the body starting in front of and behind the anus.

The qi energy flows through each meridian during the same two hours every day before passing on to the next meridian in a specified order. *Energy points* (commonly called acupuncture points) are located along the meridians or channels. Energy points can be viewed as entry portals into the energy system similar to the way in which a computer keyboard provides access to a computer.

For centuries the Chinese had no interest in trying to prove their healing system to anyone. They pragmatically observed it worked and that was enough. In recent years they began to study the energy system and energy based treatment methods scientifically. In 1990 we visited a multistory facility in Beijing were many studies of TCM techniques and herbs were underway, more or less a National Institutes of Health in TCM.

Studies conducted mainly in China, Japan and France show beyond any reasonable doubt that the energy system exists as a verifiable phenomenon. Meridians and energy points have been confirmed scientifically in many ways including the use of electronic detection equipment and high voltage photography.

Existence of the meridian system also has been confirmed by tracking the course of radioactive materials injected into energy points. Professor Kim Bong Han injected the energy points of animals with a radioisotope of phosphorus and discovered the material followed not only the path but direction of flow of the classical energy meridians (1967). In 1985 Pierre de Vernejoul of the University of Paris, along with Jean-Claude Darras, tracked the course of radioactive markers. When injected into energy points the material followed the path of classical energy meridians flowing in the direction indicated in ancient charts. When injected randomly into skin, vessels, and lymphatics the radioactive material did not migrate (injections used as controls).

These types of studies show that anyone challenging the existence of the energy system as described in Chinese Medicine has not explored the scientific literature and is not up to date. For a more elaborate excursion through the scientific literature on the existence of body energies please read Appendix VII, an article written by Paul Yanick PhD that appeared in the July 2000 edition of the *Townsend Newsletter for Physicians and Patients*.

Therefore the meridian system and energy points have been proven to be a scientific fact beyond a reasonable doubt. Proving the basic theories of Chinese Medicine is far more difficult and these have not been proven. This is not to say they are not correct. I was skeptical of these theories for years until I observed successful high-level healings that were based upon the theories and nothing more. Now, 26 years after my first exposure to Chinese Medicine, the *smirker* believes all of them even if I have no proof.

A basic concept in Chinese Medicine is that the body's vital life force energy (qi) functions as the orchestra leader of all of our chemical and genetic activities. Therefore keeping the energy system in balance and harmony is the way to stay healthy and prevent illnesses, a true preventive medicine. When balance and harmony of the energy system is disrupted our chemistry begins to fail, our resistance falters, and eventually a disease will follow (usually one to which we are genetically predisposed).

When energy balance can be restored and blockages are cleared great healing can occur because of natural healing abilities we all possess but have no way to understand, at least for now. Dr. Albert Schweitzer referred to this innate healing ability as the *little doctor inside*. In our modern culture most of us stay unbalanced all the time so the *little doctor* stays on an extended and perpetual vacation.

The Miracle of Chinese Qigong

Qigong (pronounced chee goong) is the jewel of Chinese Medicine, its most powerful healing method. The basic principles of qigong originated in India 4,000 years ago, passed through Tibet and matured in China. Qigong evolved in isolation and secrecy among elite groups such as Buddhist monks, intellectuals and the Emperor's physicians. As a result several thousands of ways of practicing qigong developed. Common steps among most of the methods include breathing with the abdomen (diaphragm), stretching exercises and clearing the mind of ordinary mundane thought.

As mentioned previously, I co-authored a book on qigong (*Miracle Healing From China...Qigong*) that provides a good introduction to the subject. Some of the basic concepts about qigong can be found in Appendix V for those who wish to read more.

Ear Acupuncture and Ear Medicine

In 1975 and 1976 I traveled to Lyon, France, to take courses from Dr. Paul Nogier. Nogier was in his 60s at the time and the 35 American doctors in the 1975 class found him to be a friendly, humble and cordial man. If I had to pick one word to describe him I would say he was *gracious*. One day after class he transported all of us by bus to visit his 600 year old earth-home built into a rocky hillside above the city. The home was beautifully furnished on the inside with hardwood paneling and beveled, leaded glass windows and doors. Dr. and Mrs. Nogier treated us as honored guests.

Nogier began his course by telling how he became interested in the ear. In 1951 he saw many old people from the Mediterranean area in his medical practice that had little rectangular scars in the same area of the external ear. He inquired about the scars and heard tales of literally being *branded* by folk healers with a small red hot iron about three millimeters long. Generally the treatment was undertaken to relieve back pain and most said it worked well.

Nogier was a thorough man so he looked up historical reports of the phenomenon. He found a 1637 report of a Portuguese physician cauterizing a specific area of the ear for sciatica (low back pain). In 1717 Valsalva (a famous name in medical history) described cauterizing an area of the ear to relieve a toothache.

He began to look for skin changes in the ear and correlated these with disease patterns in his patients. One person with liver disease might have a red spot in a specific area. Then he might find three more people with liver disease who had some sort of marking in the same spot. If a person had broken a certain bone, Nogier might find some unusual marking, mole, or discoloration in the ear at a specific location and confirm this location in other patients with the same fracture. In this manner he slowly developed a map of the ear in which all parts of the body were represented.

What he discovered was a pattern in which body parts are represented in the shape of an upside-down fetus. The ear lobe represents the head and other body areas fall in line from there as you go higher up the ear.

He then developed what he called the *Punctoscope,* an electronic device in which a probe was passed over the external ear searching for active spots. The Punctoscope detected changes in skin resistance over energy points. The instrument would beep over a hot spot and Nogier then treated that location with a silver, gold or stainless steel needle, magnet, pressure, massage or other means. (See color photo section.)

He went on to discover what he called the *auriculo-cardiac reflex* (ear-heart reflex) which he detected by feeling the radial artery at the wrist. Nogier's pulse was very different than the pulse diagnosis of Chinese Medicine in which the examiner feels three superficial and three deep pulses on each radial artery, each pulse representing one of the twelve energy meridians or channels.

He asked a patient to lie down on a table on his or her

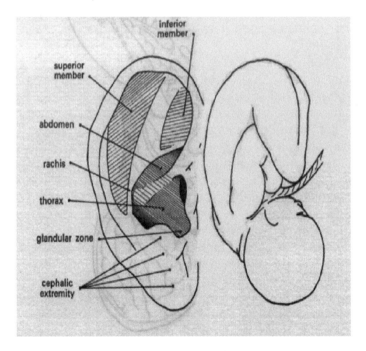

Illustration #1: Drawing showing upside-down fetus on right and corresponding general body-map areas on left. From *Handbook to Auriculotherapy* by Dr. Paul Nogier, Maisonneuve, France, 1981.

back, with the left arm raised so the hand was level with the ear. He sat in a chair at the head of the table and placed his left thumb on the patient's left radial artery (at the wrist). He sought out the spot where the pulse was strongest and in physics this is called the *peak amplitude* of the waveform. (See photo section for a simulation of how Dr. Nogier felt this pulse.)

In this testing position Nogier used his free hand to bring materials from his arm's length toward the right ear of the patient, into the patient's energy field. If the material clashed with the patient's energy field, the peak amplitude of the waveform moved slightly. He referred to this pulse change as a *peak amplitude shift*. He acknowledged it was very subtle and difficult for most people to feel.

After visiting with a group of senior veterinary acupuncturists in 2000 I learned some were using a modification of the original Nogier pulse. They feel for an increase in amplitude (strength) of the pulse when something negative enters the energy field of the animal and this appears to be far easier to detect than Nogier's variation.

Nogier demonstrated how he could diagnose cancer using nothing more than a stack of microscopic slides. On each slide was a sample of ground up cancer tissue from a different organ of the body covered with a permanent cover slip. He picked up a stack of slides and slowly brought it from arm's length toward the patient's right ear. If the stack of slides contained a slide of cancer tissue similar to a cancer in the patient's body the pulse changed abnormally. He then tested smaller groups of slides until he isolated the one responsible for the positive test. Then appropriate routine diagnostic tests were ordered for confirmation.

Nogier gave us another demonstration of his ingenious mind. He placed one of his cancer slides on a patient's abdomen and approached the right ear with a slide containing the same cancer. At first a positive response occurred in the pulse test but after about half a minute the response turned neutral. He told us the body quickly senses that the tissue on the abdomen is external and can be ignored.

Using his pulse test Nogier went on to study the effects of light and various frequencies on the body. He used a frequency generator and a hand-held probe to aim different frequencies of light at different parts of the body. He must have been astounded by the orderliness of a pattern he discovered. He found that specific body tissues were in *resonance* with specific frequencies according to their embryologic origin. This is worth repeating for I believe this single finding will one day be recognized as one of the greatest discoveries of medicine, possibly worth a Nobel Prize for Nogier. Once again, he found specific body tissues were in resonance with specific frequencies according to their embryologic origin. That's a mouthful.

A fairly complete list of tissues and corresponding resonance frequencies is provided in Appendix II. One example is that skin comes from embryologic ectodermal tissue that is in resonance with 292 Hz (cycles per second). Therefore, a cut, burn or abrasion of the skin should be treated with LEDs pulsed at 292 Hz.

The importance of Nogier's pulsed frequencies seems to have been overlooked by most researchers and manufacturers in the area of LED and LLLT devices possibly because most have no background in Chinese Medicine theories or acupuncture. There may be only five manufacturers in the world making LED and laser devices using Nogier's frequencies and most research done with LLLT has used un-pulsed devices. When pulsed frequencies are used they often appear to have been selected at random or determined by properties of the equipment.

Nogier went on to develop a method of using his pulse test and a frequency generator to diagnose which tissue was in trouble. He showed us how a right lower abdominal pain could be distinguished as originating in abdominal wall tissue (in resonance with mesodermal tissues, or 1,168 Hz) or in the gastrointestinal tract (in resonance with endodermal tissue, or 584 Hz). This and other more complicated steps with colored filters and pulsed colors were developed into a comprehensive diagnostic and

83

treatment system he called *ear medicine* that he taught in four levels.

Nogier offered a basic theory of sickness and healing. When we become ill, cells, molecules, or particles of matter are out of their normal resonance, or vibratory pattern. They often can

Photo: Paul MF Nogier MD, circa 1981.

recover if they are exposed to their normal resonance frequencies over and over in what could be called a retraining program.

Nogier died in the early 1990s and little remains in writing of his work. He did author a little book called *Handbook to Auriculotherapy* (1981) that is hard to find and out of print. That book describes his first level of teaching, finding and treating points in the ear with his basic point finder. His colleague, Rene Bourdiol MD of Paris, wrote two texts about ear medicine including details of Nogier's auriculo-cardiac reflex test. These also are out of print and the publisher no longer is in business.

Nogier's system of ear medicine lives on among a small number of practitioners. I am aware of only one source of instruction in Nogier's system in North America, courses taught by Mikhael Adams ND of Canada (see Resources).

Rene Bourdiol MD

Rene Bourdiol MD was a co-instructor in Nogier's classes and must have had one of the first *energy medicine* practices in the world in the 1970s. In Lyon, Nogier frequently asked Bourdiol to do an iris examination of a new demonstration patient before he began his evaluation. This took all of a minute after which Nogier would announce, "Dr. Bourdiol already knows what is wrong with this patient."

In 1976 I asked Dr. Bourdiol if I could visit his office in Paris the week following Nogier's course and observe him treating patients for a day. Bourdiol spoke no English so my rusty college French got a good work out that day.

When Bourdiol greeted a patient he pulled out an instrument made by Zeiss Instruments of Germany and examined the iris of the eye (the colored area around the black opening). He had written one of about twelve books on *iridology*, the mapping of corresponding body parts in the iris, most written by Europeans. I found him to be more meticulous than others because in developing his map he took photos of the iris of 8,000 patients and cross-correlated changes with known diseases, similar to how Nogier worked out his map of the ear.

Bourdiol's book contains hundreds of color photos of irises. Iris diagnosis is scoffed at in this country, but a professor of anatomy at the University of Paris Medical School wrote the preface for his book in which he declared the findings to be indisputable.

This day a young lady entered with symptoms of a persistent headache for a month. Iris examination of one eye revealed the findings of an outward pointing *spike* in the T-5 area of her spine (in the chest).

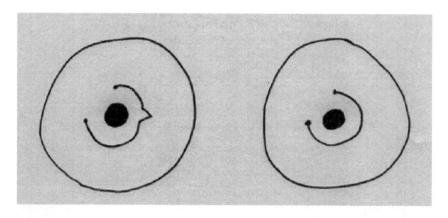

Illustration #2: Iris of left eye before treatment (on left) and after treatment (on right). The dark circle in the middle represents the pupil through which light passes to the retina. The three/quarter circle located one third of the way from the pupil to the outside of the iris (with the spike pointing to the right side of the drawing) represents the spine according to the mapping system of Bourdiol.

Bourdiol drew the spine line with the spike and asked me to look and remember what it looked like. The spike was very easy to see. Then he performed an osteopathic manipulation at T-5 in a specific direction as indicated by the direction of the spike. He said

86

if the spike had pointed inward he would have adjusted in the opposite direction. We looked at her iris again and the spike was gone as was the headache. He said I was lucky to see this case because abnormal findings in the iris go back to normal only if an event is recent and most of his patients have chronic problems.

Aime Limoge and Electroanesthesia

While in Paris I visited another French scientist, Aime Limoge MD. Limoge was working on a US Army funded grant advancing research in electro-anesthesia (full general anesthesia using electricity). What the Army was looking for was a little black box that could put a soldier under a general anesthetic in a surgical tent by flipping a switch.

Limoge's research had not reached that level, but he had a large study underway at the University of Paris Medical School Hospital. He took me to the surgery suite, introduced me to the anesthesiologist and a surgeon, and left me there all day to observe two cases.

The *black box* was a sophisticated electronic gadget that proudly wore the logo of the multinational conglomerate ITT. Electric wires led from the unit to EKG type skin pads that were placed on three energy points on the head, one between the brows and two behind the ears (Limoge said his work was based on acupuncture). In the back of the box was a covered locked switch that determined if current from the instrument actually went to the patient or not. The switch was turned either on or off according to a random design by a research technician who visited the operating suite before each case. Position of the switch was not revealed to people in the surgery suite.

The patients first were given a general anesthetic in the usual manner with a tube in the windpipe. Then the anesthesiologist turned on a switch on the front of the device. Lights blinked on and off and a waveform appeared on a screen. The instrument had this appearance in all cases whether or not current went to the electrodes on the patient.

That day one patient got the real current; the other was in the control group. In the placebo case larger doses of drugs were required as the surgery progressed. The patient receiving the electric current required progressively lower drug doses to maintain an adequate level of anesthesia and very small doses were needed toward the end. About 30 minutes into the surgery the anesthesiologist joked about how easy it was to tell this patient was receiving current. He had very little to do after the first hour and that made his job very easy.

The end of the case was equally as dramatic. As the final skin stitch was tied the machine was turned off and the patient awoke instantly. She heard my 8 mm movie camera running, raised her head about a foot off of the table and looked squarely into the lens. Never have I seen a patient wake up from a general anesthetic suddenly, alert and aware.

The best was yet to come. Patients who received the current experienced no pain for the first sixteen hours following surgery. During that time they walked around the ward normally and were encouraged to breath deeply. When the grace period ended they needed narcotic doses similar to what control patients were receiving at sixteen hours. With early ambulation they experienced far fewer problems with blood clots and infections than those receiving the placebo current.

By the time of my visit (1976) the hospital had performed over 1,000 cases with the current, but Limoge seemed depressed. He told me the US Army was not happy with his progress and funding may come to an end. Apparently those in charge of funding had little appreciation of the progress Limoge had made. I never heard of the technique again.

Reinhold Voll MD

German physician Reinhold Voll was a contemporary of Nogier. Voll developed an elaborate diagnostic and treatment system he called *electroacupuncture according to Voll,* or *EAV.* Central to his system is the *Dermatron*, an instrument that takes

88

readings on energy points. When abnormal readings are obtained various homeopathic remedies are brought into the circuit with the patient. When beneficial remedies are tested abnormal readings return to normal. In this manner remedies are selected and given to the patient and improvements are common. Voll began to attract patients to his Munich office from all over the world.

Voll was a meticulous man who worked with a group of 30 other MDs in the development of his system. Many of these doctors made contributions to the system and when something new was discovered they all had to confirm the new finding.

In the Chinese energy system all twelve paired meridians have end points in the sides of either fingers or toes. This left eight sides of toes and fingers blank on the energy charts of Chinese Medicine. By electronic testing Voll discovered seven energy meridians that were unknown to the Chinese. Not all are useful but some open the door to easy testing and treatment of allergies, nerve disorders, lymph drainage problems and joint problems.

I attended a course given by Dr. Voll in San Francisco in about 1978. He was a short, dogmatic little German who spoke no English. While showing slides he drove his point home by slamming his pointer against the defenseless projection screen, almost puncturing the material. Then he settled down for a moment as the translator said something like, "Dr. Voll has just emphasized that ......"

John Ott

I would be remiss in not including the importance of full spectrum light in biology. John Ott was a pioneer in this field and made many of the early time-lapse sequences used by Disney in movies such as *On a Clear Day You Can See Forever*.

Most of us are aware some plants need outdoor sun exposure full of UV light while others are killed by the same exposures and must live indoors or in perpetual shade as in a jungle. Exposure to specific wavelengths (colors) of light has been shown to have biologic effects. For example, minks grown under blue light produce 80 % female liters.

One of Ott's stories I recall best is of a contract to make a time-lapse film of an apple blossom from bloom to bright red apple. A camera was set up in a tree and a blossom was selected and protected from wind motion by a glass cage. The blossom developed into a little green apple that grew and grew. In the fall when all other apples on the tree turned red his little apple stayed green and was killed off by frost.

Ott couldn't figure out what happened so he repeated the effort the same way the next season. Once again his little apple stayed green and did not ripen. He then woke up to the fact that the glass cage was filtering out UV rays the apple needed to ripen. The third year he filmed again, but this time he used a glass cage with doors that closed only when a frame was going to be shot. That year he got his red apple.

Ott lectured at one of our environmental medicine meetings in the late 1970s. At that time he was performing muscle testing of the arm to demonstrate how various light inputs can make a person stronger or weaker. He took a huge, young, strong doctor from the audience (a former professional football player), tested him and could almost hang his weight from the horizontally held arm. He tested the doctor again as he stared at a TV monitor and the arm had no strength. Ott placed a one-inch thick grid in front of the TV screen and on a repeat test the doctor was strong. Ott said certain wavelengths of energy were coming out of the TV that weaken us and a grid of the proper depth can block the harmful ones.

Bill Rea MD

Bill Rea of Dallas, Texas, is another friend of mine who has studied the effects of various frequencies on the body. His interest began when a few patients told him that when they were near an ordinary electric outlet their hands shook uncontrollably. Rea blindfolded them for testing and verified the stories. During my practice years I was fortunate to confirm this observation in one of my own patients.

Rea tested people by exposing them to a range of frequencies produced by a frequency generator and showed videotapes of these experiments at his annual meeting. Some rare individuals experienced grand mal convulsions when specific frequencies were broadcast in their direction (they were kept lying on a hospital gurney with padded sides, with attendants and physicians present).

Jean Munro MD, a colleague of Rea's in England, carried out similar studies. We were shown a video of a man who was sensitive to emissions from high-tension power lines. The man was hooded and blindfolded, placed in the back of a van, and driven around the countryside in England. When the van passed under high tension lines he had a seizure, became unconscious and recovered when the van was a safe distance away. The same thing occurred every time the van passed under the power lines.

My wife and I were fortunate to recently vacation in England and I had a window seat as we landed at Heathrow Airport. I noticed some high tension lines passing through a city and was pleased to see bare land beneath the lines, with the nearest houses about 100 yards away. Is it possible the British are acting on information that seems clear to them but becomes muddled in the United States by lobbying efforts of power companies?

An Energy Diagnosis Instrument in Western Medicine?

In 1990 Dr. Kong took me to Harbin, Manchuria, in the northeastern part of China. We traveled there specifically to visit a family of Traditional Chinese Medical doctors that developed an interesting diagnostic machine with great potential. At that time the machine consisted of six little electronic boxes and a tangle of wires. One instrument was an oscilloscope that displays electronic waves.

As usual I volunteered to be the guinea pig. Conductive leads were hooked to my arms and legs and the TCM doctor tested body correspondence points up and down the front of my chest. Each point represented a specific organ or part. When an abnormal point was tested, there was an uncomfortable little shock at the point on the chest and the oscilloscope showed a changed waveform.

Developers described a most unusual case using the instrument. Early in their studies they tested anyone who would lie on the table long enough, such as family members, co-workers and staff. To their surprise readings on their 30 year-old secretary indicated an early stomach cancer. Because TCM doctors and western doctors cooperate with each other they arranged for the lady to be gastroscoped (a visual examination of the stomach) but nothing was found. This pattern was repeated every two months until at six months a little red area was seen, biopsied and was found positive for stomach cancer. The instrument detected the cancer when it was nothing more than a twinkle of a defect in the energy system.

The instrument has another application. When a treatment is instituted the waveform on the oscilloscope shows instant changes toward improvement if the treatment is going to be effective. If the treatment is not going to work the instrument continues to show the original abnormal waveform potentially saving valuable time spent in trial and error treatments.

Such an instrument could bring vast improvements to medicine. It could be used anytime there is confusion in diagnosing, narrowing a problem down to where only a few tests may be needed. It certainly could save a lot of money if it allowed doctors to avoid shot-gunning tests that often cost in the thousands of dollars. It could also be used to evaluate patients in whom some treatment has begun.

As of this date I have heard nothing further about the development of the machine. In the early 1990s no progress was being made for lack of funds.

Ultraviolet Light

The first time I entered a premature nursery as a student in the 1950s I was shown a tiny naked baby lying in an incubator with its eyes covered. The nurse told us the baby was under an ultraviolet light.

Premature babies are placed under a UV light source to prevent bilurubin levels from going too high in the blood. Bilirubin is a compound found in normal red blood cells that is released during the continual breakdown and recycling of red blood cells. The liver normally processes bilirubin, but in premature babies it may be too immature to do the job. If levels go too high permanent brain damage occurs. After a few days the liver generally matures enough to process bilirubin and the crisis is over.

Anyone who questions whether shining LEDs on the skin may work should be reminded of this long standing and orthodox treatment of premature babies.

The Abstracts of Steinman

Ralph Steinman DDS was a researcher at the Loma Linda University School of Dentistry and published in the 1960s a collection of research papers pertaining to oral health. These appeared in several obscure dental research journals and the collection was printed in a pamphlet called *Abstracts of Steinman* (no date). I would like to review some of his work here as it relates to energy balances in the body.

Steinman spent years studying something that was never mainstreamed into the curriculum of our dental schools, the fluid flow in teeth. When animals are well and in a good state of health a fluid flows from the inside to the outside of teeth and this helps wash debris and food away preventing decay. When animals are out of normal healthy balance, the flow reverses and sucks debris onto the surface of the tooth, which promotes decay.

Steinman's tools were simple. He did various things to animals such as placing dye in the mouth, abdominal cavity or tail vein and then pulled teeth over a period of time, cut them in cross section, and observed movement of the dye.

When he injected refined sugar solution in the abdominal cavity of rats the fluid flow shifted to the undesirable outside-in pattern. In another experiment he placed refined sugar in the mouths of weanling rats but stopped doing so before any teeth erupted. When the teeth came in they rotted away even though sugar never made direct contact with any teeth.

This is the real reason I include Steinman's work. In the field of nutrition a debate has lingered on for years about the safety of refined sugar. Nutrition experts and chemists examine refined sugar and see a six-carbon molecule that looks the same in a sugar cane plant or sugar beet as in a bag of sugar in the store or in your dessert. In Steinman's experiments when rats were exposed to refined sugar bad things happened. It is likely the refining process alters normal resonance frequencies of sugar and this disrupts energy balance in the consumer. At present this is hard to confirm in a way scientists would accept.

During one of our visits to Hawaii we toured a sugar refinery. During the tour we learned how the cane plants were crushed and boiled in large vats to separate out the sugar. I asked how the huge pots were cleaned and was told they used a formaldehyde solution. Possibly formaldehyde, heat or other practices unknown to us can change the electromagnetic properties of refined sugar in a way that causes it to become harmful to our energy system.

Steinman's concept is easy to demonstrate on your own body. Try going for three or four days without eating any refined sugar, including any processed foods that contain refined sugar. Brush and floss your teeth each night at bedtime and first thing in the morning scrape a fingernail along the base of the teeth. If your body is in reasonable balance the teeth will feel clean to the tongue and no debris will accumulate under the fingernail.

On the next day pig out on some ice cream, pie, cake, or junk foods. At bedtime clean your teeth in the same manner. The next morning run your tongue across your teeth. Most people will

94

discover the teeth will feel coated with debris sticking to them that can be scraped off with the fingernail, usually a white material.

Maintaining a normal fluid flow in teeth very well could be a reason why primitive natives visited by Weston Price DDS in the 1930s had such good oral health. Refined carbohydrates and sugar were not available to them and they remained almost totally free of tooth decay until junk foods arrived in their lives.

Harmful Energies

In most of this book we have been talking about the positive effects of subtle energies. We should not forget that there are harmful energies out there as well.

Far frequencies of ultraviolet light are harmful. These rays from the sun are making the news today because depletion of the ozone layer is thinning protective layers in the atmosphere and skin cancers are on the increase. Those who don't accept this connection should try explaining why skin cancer rates were far lower when most of us were working under the hot sun on farms.

Excessive amounts of X-rays are harmful, but for years medicine remained blasé about the risks. When I was a young boy (age six to ten) our shoe store used a fluoroscopic (X-ray) machine to test the fit of shoes. Children formed a long line waiting to play with the machine whenever it was not in use by sales people. We pushed the *on* button to watch our toes wiggle inside our shoes never suspecting we were exposing ourselves to harmful X-rays.

In medical school in 1958 I saw radiologists pushing barium through patients' GI tracts with their bare hands, with the fluoroscopy machine on continuously dosing themselves with X-rays. Shortly afterward statistics appeared showing high rates of skin cancer in the hands of radiologists and they began to take precautions. Fortunately, new X-ray machines expose us to far smaller doses.

Microwaves are harmful. This is the reason your microwave oven shuts off when the door is opened. Even with that

95

safety feature it is wise to stay eight to ten feet away from it when on in case the door is defective. We speculate that when qigong masters kill bacteria by holding test tubes of cultures they are doing so by emitting microwaves.

High-tension lines appear to have health risks, though the debate goes on. Many double blind studies have been published showing leukemia rates double in children who live in the vicinity of high-tension lines.

As we are about to go to print we are hearing about the potential danger of cell phones. There are reports that if the antenna of a cell phone is too close to the head abnormal and harmful irradiation may increase the incidence of brain cancer, a serious worry.

Summary

What can we learn from all of this? First of all, the body is alive with subtle energies and some people have been able to tap into this knowledge and develop treatment systems based on the information. Some of these are based on body correspondence maps that have been found on the skin. Maps not mentioned so far include those on the nose, tongue, hand and foot. Tongue diagnosis is used in Traditional Chinese Medicine, a palm acupuncture system was developed in Korea, and reflexologists use the foot map.

Even conventional physicians are aware of one referred pain connection but don't appreciate its connection with TCM. It is common for people with gall bladder disease to have a pain in their right temple directly over Gall Bladder #7 on the gall bladder meridian.

The energies are subtle. Most people clobber the energy system, wonder why they become ill, and expect a quick fix from mass applied treatment approaches that have nothing to do with why they became ill in the first place.

CHAPTER 8: INSTANT HEALING

This is my favorite subject, one that has fascinated me for years. When I strayed far from the dogma of western medicine in 1974 I began to try out new treatments on my patients. Some of my most enjoyable experiences occurred when I treated other doctors' *treatment failures* with some wild new therapy and got a beneficial response quickly, sometimes instantly. I view these responses as demonstrations of the body's energy system at work as the orchestra leader of our chemistry, genetics and literally everything else, the controller of little switches in our bodies that keep everything regulated and finely tuned. Examples of instant (or at the least very rapid) healing follow.

Stinging Insect Reaction Relieved With Acupuncture

This personal experience is related in the chapter called *Energy Trek*. In summary, I almost died from a severe allergic reaction to a fire ant bite in New Orleans in 1968 and frequently after such a reaction any venom may have serious or even fatal effects. In 1974 a yellow jacket stung my palm and soon my thumb, index and middle fingers swelled to the size of large sausages. Simple acupuncture needles were ineffective so I attached leads from an electronic stimulation device to the needles. When I pushed the *on* button my hand turned from red to white as if a switch had been thrown and all reactions from the sting were gone within 30 minutes.

Genital Herpes Relieved With Acupuncture

In 1968 I was working as a gynecologist in a Kaiser HMO facility in California when I saw a woman with painful ulcers all over her genitals. I asked ten other gynecologists to look at her and we all were dumfounded. We sent her to the dermatology clinic and soon the dermatologist called to tell us she had a case of herpes.

No gynecologist in our clinic had seen a similar case and it was not described in specialty textbooks or journals. Before long this diagnosis was common and within a few short years 500,000 new cases were reported per year in the United States. There was no effective treatment and women were forced to suffer with painful genital ulcers until they healed, which took about three weeks. Later, often during periods of stress or illness, the ulcers would recur because the virus was only sleeping (dormant), not dead.

This is an excellent example of a virus undergoing a mutation into a form that produces a new disease. This is also a good reason to learn how to pump up your own immune defense system because antibiotics are not going to bail us out forever (they don't work on viruses now).

In 1974 I began to use my electronic acupuncture instrument on women who would do anything to experience relief of severe pain. When I entered the exam room I found them lying on their sides because pain and swelling prevented them from sitting normally on the exam table.

I inserted needles in energy points on the insides of the knees and turned on the instrument. Within ten minutes about 90% of these women hopped off the table with a smile. They squatted, jumped, sat and moved around not believing the pain could go away so quickly. Many called later to report the ulcers healed in about half the time expected (seven to ten days instead of three weeks).

Excessive Vaginal Lubrication Relieved With Ear Acupuncture

In 1975, not long after I took Nogier's ear acupuncture course in France, a young woman was referred to me by another gynecologist as a treatment failure. She had a vaginal discharge for months, was tested and treated over and over during ten visits to my friend until he ran out of ideas. The discharge just went on and on requiring use of a napkin 24 hours a day.

After trying two additional approaches that failed I sat her down and asked her to tell me exactly what her problem felt like to her in her own words. She said it was like her sexual vaginal lubrication system was switched on but wouldn't turn off.

That rang a bell. In France Dr. Nogier taught us that there was a specific point in the ear that controlled this mechanism like a switch. I looked up my old notes, treated that point with a needle and her drainage problem stopped. End of problem.

Muscle Spasm Relief With a Pulsed Magnet

During the years I was delivering babies I saw many women who suffered muscle spasms in the back as the baby grew bigger and bigger. We could offer little relief because of a desire to avoid using drugs during pregnancy.

One woman, seven months pregnant, suffered from a muscle spasm down the right side of her back for over a month. On exam I saw that the muscle was tight while the same muscle on the other side was soft and relaxed. I told her I wanted to try a treatment I learned in France but because it was unorthodox I didn't even want her to see what I was doing. She trusted me and agreed to these unusual terms.

I brought out Dr. Nogier's *Therapuncteur* instrument. A wire leads out of one port on the machine to a hand held probe with a tip about the size of a pencil lead. The probe delivers a pulsed magnetic energy at much lower frequencies than Nogier's other devices.

I switched the machine to frequency C (10 Hz) for connective tissue (muscles and joints) and with her clothes on passed the probe over the spasm area for ten minutes as she faced the wall in front of her. The probe never touched the skin and she couldn't tell when the treatment began or ended. When I finished she said the pain was gone and I confirmed that the muscle was soft. The problem did not recur during the remainder of her pregnancy.

An Iris Abnormality Reversed With Spinal Adjustment

As mentioned (in the chapter titled *Energy Trek*) I visited the office of Rene Bourdiol MD in Paris, France, in 1976 to observe him in action because he had a unique medical practice. Dr. Bourdiol was practicing *Energy Medicine* 100% of the time by then and had written books in iridology (diagnosing energy disturbances by examination of the iris of the eye) and osteopathic spinal manipulation or *manual medicine*. When, in the late 1970s, the University of Southern California School of Medicine sponsored a training program in osteopathic manipulation Bourdiol was flown in as an instructor.

A young woman entered Bourdiol's office complaining of a severe two-week, one-sided headache. Bourdiol looked at her irises with a magnifying scope (Zeiss) and said, "Ah, hah." He drew a sketch of an abnormality in the form of a spike he saw on a circle line in the left iris and asked me to verify this with the scope. He said this represented a mechanical problem at T-5 of her thoracic spine that called for a manipulation. Because the defect was in one eye and pointed outward the manipulation called for was in one specific direction.

Bourdiol asked the woman to lie on his treatment table as he did a simple painless manipulation on her back. When she got up she said her headache was gone.

When we looked at the left eye again the spike in the spine line of the iris was gone. He told me this response is seen only when the problem has a very short history. When a problem becomes chronic the iris pattern is fixed forever, forming a permanent record of the injury.

Remembering this case makes me think of a probable mechanism of how spinal manipulation by chiropractors and osteopaths may work. A subtle injury may cause muscles between vertebrae to lock up the joint and this upsets the energy balance in that area or elsewhere. Moving or stretching the muscles (the manipulation) can release the blocks and relieve symptoms not only locally, but also in distant places because energy meridians described in Traditional Chinese Medicine pass throughout the body and frequently connect with each other. This may explain why 100 years ago chiropractors began to believe and were taught they could relieve problems in all parts of the body with their spinal manipulation.

Instant Responses With Allergy Extracts

In the 1940s ENT doctor Herbert Rinkel developed a new approach to testing allergy extracts called the *Rinkel technique* (also called serial dilution titration testing). In this technique one to five serial dilutions of extracts are made. Bottle #1 is a 1:5 dilution, bottle #2 is a 1:25 dilution, bottle #3 is a 1:125 dilution, bottle #4 is a 1:625 dilution, and so on.

Rinkel himself worked out the system when he was using standard allergy testing methods on a man who had hay fever due to ragweed. I heard Rinkel lecture in 1976 and he described how he applied a single skin test of ragweed extract and the man's hay fever symptoms stopped instantly. This led him to test different dilutions of extracts on many people trying all possible dilution schemes between 1:10 to 1:5.

Something magical happened with the 1:5 dilution series extracts. He began with a #6 bottle and injected a constant volume into the skin (an intra-dermal test). If no swelling occurred within ten minutes he injected the next stronger concentrated #5 dilution and so on until the bump produced by the injection enlarged at least two millimeters within ten minutes. He found that each stronger dilution injected after that produced swelling that was 2 mm greater in diameter than the previous test, at least in most people. It sounds as complicated as it is.

In my allergy practice (1976 to 1985) I frequently confirmed Rinkel's findings in people with sensitivities to inhalants, animal danders, and molds, as well as with foods and chemical compounds. I want to tell you about two other special uses of the technique.

When I was practicing gynecology patients frequently came to the office with severe menstrual cramps. I found I could inject a natural progesterone extract (synthetics didn't work) in the one to five series and by trial and error find a dose that would relieve the cramps in a minute or two. My technician placed this dilution into a bottle for home use as drops under the tongue and this worked as well as the injection given in the office. Many women swore by it.

Another example is in the treatment of the flu. A patient of mine developed the flu while in the hospital following surgery. I went to the ward and tried several dilutions of an extract made from common flu vaccine. One dilution completely relieved the aches, pains and headache within a minute. I don't believe the nurses ever quite understood what happened or why.

Qigong and Instant Relief of Paralysis

In 1988 I saw qigong master Xia Lei-ming treat a man for the first time in a neighborhood clinic in Beijing. The man had suffered a stroke eighteen months previously that left both arms and legs paralyzed. When he tried to speak he produced only grunts and groans. For lack of a gurney his sons carried him, seated in a chair, into the makeshift clinic. Both of his arms were contracted at the elbows with motion constricted, all fingers were tightly locked and flexed, and both legs were contracted at the knees.

This was his first treatment. The qigong master worked on him for about 20 minutes and then manually straightened out the four contracted extremities as the patient groaned with discomfort. The sons were asked to get dad up so he could walk around. They reluctantly complied fearing he would fall and at one point he leaned so far to one side he almost did. Once on his feet he slowly and awkwardly walked around the room twice, and then was asked to do two partial deep knee bends. After the second knee bend the poor fellow smiled and groaned with happiness.

102

Remember, this is a 60-year old man who had not been out of bed for eighteen months following a severe stroke.

This is but one of many cases of instant success with qigong I have seen with my own eyes. In Spokane qigong master Hu got three people moving paralyzed limbs after working on them for about an hour each. One woman had a paralyzed arm for one month. A second woman was paralyzed in both legs for seven years. One man had been paralyzed in the legs and living in a nursing home for 36 years following a spinal cord injury in motorcycle accident.

In Appendix V on Chinese qigong I relate several miraculous cures by qigong master Yan Xin. One of Yan Xin's most famous cases was of a man with a spinal cord injury who had not walked for eight months following an industrial accident. Yan Xin treated him for eight hours from ten kilometers away. The man slept for nine hours, then got up and walked around his home with a crutch. Several months later he walked up the Great Wall with the qigong master on national television.

Of all the healing modalities I have seen and experienced on three continents in 30 years qigong applied by a powerful master tops them all.

Pulsed Light Improves Vision

I would like to mention a case reported by Jacob Liberman OD PhD in his book *Light, Medicine of the Future*. Liberman saw a young girl who had 20/20 vision in one eye and 20/200 in the other. He flashed (pulsed?) a bright light into her 20/20 eye for 30 minutes then repeated the vision test. The eye with 20/200 vision improved to 20/25. After five more similar treatments vision in the weak eye was 20/20 and held at that level for years.

Pulsed Light and Corneal Ulcers

Marvin Cain DVM treats racehorses and says it is common during a race for one horse to kick up dirt and rocks into the eye of another horse causing a corneal ulcer (an area of raw surface in the covering of the middle of the eye through which we see). Routine treatment is similar to treatment in humans with antibiotics and immobility, taping the lid closed for a few days.

When Dr. Cain began to use pulsed LEDs in 1982 he tried the method on a horse with a fresh corneal ulcer that was very deep. He used a pad containing infrared LEDs pulsed at Nogier's frequency A for skin problems (ectoderm) for a few minutes. A few hours later he checked the horse and could see the edges growing in forming a new covering. By morning a thin fresh new layer of skin covered the ulcer, a finding usually not seen in less than five to seven days. Marvin says he has treated literally hundreds of horses and small animals with similar results.

Pulsed Light and Cuts and Abrasions

Hearing Dr. Cain's story of rapid healing I began to use a small hand-held pulsed LED instrument to treat minor problems such as aches, pains, cuts, bruises and burns. My four year-old grandson has been the biggest user because he seems to bounce off some hard object or fall down every hour. When we use the light on him he says the pain is gone in only ten to fifteen seconds. When he gets bumped again he comes asking for "the light." A testimonial from a four year old may not carry much weight so I'll give you another.

One day I scrapped several layers of skin off a finger on an area of jagged broken chrome on a vehicle. I used the pulsed light on the setting for skin (A for ectoderm) and was amazed when the wound healed in two days. Healing was so complete I couldn't find any evidence of the cut.

CHAPTER 9: MYSTERIOUS QIGONG MASTER HU

Qigong master Hu (pronounced Who) came to Spokane in late1999. Hu's natural healing abilities were apparent by the time he was twelve. He then built on his natural gift with years of study and practice to become a doctor of qigong.

We found Hu to be intuitive, creative, and endowed with powerful healing abilities. He says when he is fresh and rested he can see the energy system of the body, similar to what must have occurred thousands of years ago when the meridians and points were first described in ancient China.

Hu evaluates a patient by looking for imbalances and blockages of energy flow. He closes his eyes, holds his ballpoint pen in front of him horizontally at arm's length and scans energy fields. From what he sees he develops an approach to treatment based on the theories of Chinese Medicine. Everyone is treated differently. When he sees energy disturbances are corrected he stops treating and asks the client to check things out.

For those unfamiliar with the concepts of Chinese Medicine I should say a word about the difference between energy imbalances and blockages. Imbalances are the first problems to occur, the easiest to correct, and lead to discomforts and minor diseases. Chinese Medicine doctors use the term *imbalance* to describe a condition where one energy channel has too much energy and another has too little. The job of the doctor of Chinese Medicine is to move energy from the channel with the excess to the channel with the deficiency. When this is accomplished and all meridians are in balance the problem goes away until the person gets out of balance again.

Blocks are more serious and usually are associated with diseases on a par with paralysis and cancer. An analogy would be if the wiring in your home developed a short circuit part of your house may be without electricity and serious harm may occur such as a fire. Qigong masters visualize energy blocks as black holes (about one inch in diameter) in the normal energy field of the body (aura). Qigong is believed to be the only treatment system powerful enough to *dredge* energy meridians and clear blocks.

powerful enough to *dredge* energy meridians and clear blocks. When Hu is treating someone with energy blocks and sees they have cleared, he knows the biggest part of the problem is behind him.

The very first day I met Hu he treated Kathy with qigong for about an hour and she began to move legs that had not moved for over seven years. He produced a similar series of remarkable responses in others, many going beyond what is believed to be possible by western doctors. It was like being back in China visiting one qigong facility or master after another and I enjoyed it.

Before Hu appeared on the scene Rodger had been pulling off his own little miracle healings. As a result Rodger and I were developing the idea of creating and publicizing a new healing system consisting of simple energy-delivering devices and the smaller the number and less expensive the better. We were looking for devices anyone could use to achieve inexpensive and effective healing. Rodger had been drifting in this direction for some time before he asked me to become involved.

Hu showed us he is different than the many qigong masters we had met previously. The first time I sat down with him he took out a pen and attempted to draw an electronic device that could treat people with different variations of chi, the elusive undefined energy of qigong healing, said to be our very own life force. Here was a qigong master who was interested in gadgets, possibly the only one in the world! In previous experiences I learned most qigong masters have no tolerance for electronic trinkets that produce energies of lower (hence inferior) quality than their own high level and elusive qigong energy.

The instrument Hu drew had a small dish similar to an eighteen-inch diameter satellite receiver. He said the device would pick up energy from *out there* (he pointed out the window to the sky), modify it through a software program, and deliver it through several small panels, each one specific for treating a major disease. This reminded me of how many qigong masters end up specialize in diseases they treat better than others. He tried to

106

explain how this device could create a waveform he identified as the mysterious energy of qigong.

Apparently designing such an instrument had been one of his goals for a long time. However, when I pressed him for details or a schematic, he came up short. He said our electrical engineering friends would be able to figure this out, but when I asked them they didn't have a clue. We wondered where we were headed. Fortunately, many sessions followed in the next ten weeks and more promising designs followed.

At that time Rodger was using blankets of pulsed red LEDs on clients and a pulsed infrared LED hand-held device made for animal use. We asked Hu to test them on his body and give us an opinion of their value as healing tools. Hu had never encountered any light emitting devices (LEDs) previously, especially ones that are pulsed on and off according to the frequencies of Dr. Nogier. He liked the effect different frequencies had on his energy.

We discovered his body functioned as a finely tuned testing instrument. I blindfolded him and aimed a hand-held infrared LED device at an energy point on the Large Intestine meridian in the tip of the index finger from about two centimeters away. Hu pointed to where the LEDs were aimed at his Large Intestine meridian point and traced the course and speed of the energy as it traveled up the meridian to his upper lip and on to the opposite side of the upper lip. This is the route of the Large Intestine meridian and he indicated the energy took about five to ten seconds to travel from the beginning of the meridian to the end.

We exposed the same energy point to each of the three embryologic related frequencies of Nogier (A, B, and C). Hu identified frequency B as the best one for treatment of that meridian (Large Intestine=embryonic endoderm=frequency B) and this matches what Nogier taught and veterinarians have confirmed in animals since 1982. We went on to test the LED device on the Heart and Small Intestine meridians with similar results. Hu selected the treatment frequency he said would be best for each meridian and in each case his choice coincided with information from other sources. During the testing I changed the frequency of the device several times either up or down. In each case Hu told us the direction of the change.

What happened during that session took me completely by surprise. I had never heard of anyone using a qigong master as a sensitive testing instrument in this manner.

In future sessions I asked many questions and spent much time waiting for translations. During this time Hu sat at the dining room table toying with a variety of acupuncture devices from Rodger's collection or drawing his schematic of the elusive energy of qi over and over.

I asked him if there might be some benefit from oral use of a clean probe from Rodger's anal heater. Dr. Cain (the veterinarian) first suggested this use of the heater and I quickly saw how the energy concepts of Chinese Medicine led him to this conclusion. Hu said this was a good idea.

He put a new clean probe in his mouth, turned up the heat, and indicated with a finger where he felt the energy move down the midline of his neck into the chest, then a bit to the left of center over the heart. He said this use would be good for the heart; in fact it would be better for the heart than when used in the anus. It also would stimulate the immune system because the conception vessel channel passes over the thymus and sternum with its bone marrow, both active participants in immune functions.

Hu inserted the heater into his nose. He said using the heater in the nostril would clear the nasal passages during allergic reactions. One woman at the table tried this by inserting a heater probe in each nostril and the next day reported her allergy related nasal drainage dried up for eighteen hours.

Hu inserted a probe in the canal of his ear and said this use would be good for small children with ear infections as well as for ringing in the ears (tinnitus). Joy Tang volunteered she had suffered with tinnitus in her right ear for six months after being exposed to loud noise at a rock concert. She stuck the heater probe in the troublesome ear for a few minutes and reported the ringing stopped. To this date she has had no recurrence of tinnitus for six months.

One day Hu wore himself out working on many people and his personal life was giving him problems. He got out of balance and asked Rodger for help. Rodger asked him to lie down on a treatment table under a dog pad of pulsed LEDs and inserted heater probes in both his anus and mouth at the same time. Rodger sat by Hu's side cycling impulses of the LEDs through the seven frequencies of Nogier. It was a strange sight. Rodger also gave him a qigong treatment, emitting energy from his hands. In fifteen minutes Hu was charged up, back in balance and ready to perform super-healing again.

Rodger was trying to keep his list of devices for healing down to a small number. He recently stopped using an infrasound-generating instrument so I asked Hu if we could also stop using the infrared sauna because of its high cost. Hu began to talk about something else as if he didn't hear the question or else wanted to change the subject.

He pointed to the currently available dog blanket with pulsed LEDs (all red) and said in its current form this design had a healing ability of 50% compared to healing with qi. He drew a new design and predicted it would have 90% of the healing ability of qi.

The new device had a line of white LEDs down the middle that would lie on the midline energy meridians of the front and back of the body (Conception Vessel and Governing Vessel). The next row on each side would lie over the Kidney (front) and Bladder (back) meridians and would be blue. The outside row on each side would be red.

At this time (January of 2000) blue LEDs had been available for only five years and white LEDs for only a few months. How Hu knew anything about them, especially the white, is difficult to fathom as he neither speaks nor reads English.

Given the accuracy of Hu's sensitivities and healing abilities, we were inclined to give his new ideas a try. I contacted Dave Melone who offered to make prototypes so we could fine tune them on Hu's body and also try them on some seriously ill people. Hu was predicting almost a cure-all effect and it was taking on the aroma of snake oil (actually, snake oil contains essential fatty acids, no trans fats, and has been given a bum rap).

I posed a major question. Would we one day be able to build devices that would have the full healing powers of a high-level qigong master? Hu looked at me, smiled, then said this was impossible. He said we are building devices that heal with light but the energy of qigong is on a higher plane and is different.

He took out a pad and pencil and drew his conception of the energy of qigong, a spiral through which a straight-line energy passes. Many times he drew this pattern in the air with a finger or on his legal pad with a pen. He demonstrated the straight-line part of his drawing by aiming his right finger at his left palm and as the finger approached he made a sound like sssssssssssssssssssssstt with the volume increasing as the finger and hand met.

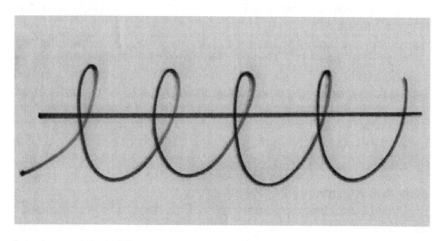

Illustration: Energy of qigong as drawn by qigong master Hu.

In late January we received the first prototype of an instrument designed by Hu, a hand held device with a triangular design of LED lights in patriotic American colors of red, white and blue. Hu experimented with the device like a playful child, eager to test it out on his body and other people and objects, on anything.

Hu fell in love with the device and told us it was delivering an energy that was close to qigong energy and such a device had never been built before. We aimed it through eight feet of concrete in my fireplace and Hu and Rodger felt the energy coming through the other side. Someone held it behind my chest and Hu and Rodger said they could see the energy coming out of the other side of my body. I pointed it at the palm of several friends and most felt warmth, a cool breeze or a tingling in the fingers. Only a few said they felt nothing. My skeptical wife felt warmth. I myself felt a cool breeze on my skin wherever I pointed the light. Those who felt warmth were surprised to touch the LEDs and find they were not warm.

Hu told us if the device illuminated objects at least 60 feet away the energy would pass through a lead shield and if it did so it could treat AIDs. We went outside at night and found the LEDs lit up my chicken coop 90 feet away. The next day we took the instrument to the office of a friendly dentist where four of us (including the dentist) felt the energy passing through a double thickness of lead blankets used to protect patients from X-rays. Hu said that in China the progress of students of qigong is measured by asking them to emit their qi through a lead plate as instructors line up their hands in a row on the other side to feel how much energy is coming through.

I tried to reproduce the experience we had several weeks before when we aimed a hand-held pulsed infrared LED device at meridians on Hu's hand. I placed my parka over Hu's head so he could not see and shined the new device at a meridian on one of his fingers. He was undecided for a minute and then wiggled a distant finger. We tried again and again with similar results.

Hu threw off the parka in frustration and looked puzzled. When we shined the LEDs on his index finger he said he could feel the energy spread out in all directions equally. Therefore, all fingers were receiving the same amount of energy so he couldn't tell where the device was aimed.

111

Then I asked him how fast the energy was passing up his arm. He aimed the device at an energy point near a fingernail and said the energy went up his arm instantly. Hu and Rodger then visually examined the light coming from the LEDs and saw little spirals of energy of all colors of the spectrum going in all directions.

I asked Hu how powerful this device was and where we stood now in terms of healing potential compared to qi. He smiled and said we had in our hands a device that delivered energy very *similar* to the energy of qigong, far above the 90% healing level he previously predicted. I was delighted and joked to all present I was holding in my hands a *qigong master in a box.*

Hu was mentally working on a design for a new device he said might cure AIDs. Now that we knew energy from the device passed through a lead shield he was more certain. This is quite an impertinent prediction and only trial and error will tell on this one. Our job in the future will be to conduct trials to see if his devices live up to his grandiose claims for cures and functions. We are willing to take him seriously for now because of what we have seen all ready. If everything Hu predicted to us comes to pass he should receive a Nobel Prize for Medicine.

(See a photo of qigong masters Hu and Rodger in color photo section)

CHAPTER 10: THEORIES OF HOW THE PROGRAM WORKS

After observing unexpectedly powerful healing, curious people try to explain why and how it may occur. Some explanations are obvious, others theoretical. We believe the modalities and energies involved (heat, pulsed LED lights, infrared sauna, minerals) help establish a normal energetic balance in the body; at least that is their intended use. How and why they work synergistically defies explanation.

Nutrients are Important

This is not a book on nutrition so at this time I only wish to stress the importance of being adequately nourished in trace minerals. It is widely accepted that it is difficult to achieve a healing response if a person is grossly malnourished. It is our opinion (Rodger's and mine) that our cells are probably more deficient in trace minerals than other nutrients. Factors leading to this state of under-nutrition are many and originated in our culture over the past 200 years. However, it appears more is going than can be blamed on straightforward nutritional deficiencies alone.

In my first book, *How to Survive Modern Technology (1979),* I described how our modern diseases of physical degeneration (i.e. heart attacks, strokes, high blood pressure, diabetes, and a long list of others) were not observed in *isolated* primitive life style people as long as they had an adequate food supply. However, when a store opens selling refined and processed foods, oral problems (decay and crooked teeth) appear within a year or two and other diseases show up after a lag period of 20-30 years that obscures the connection. This was seen in settings where only 10 to 15% of the food supply came from outside the area because this was all these people could afford on meager wages. Something else had to be going on.

As we have seen, everything has a resonance frequency right down to the smallest sub-atomic particles. It is very likely the

113

resonance frequencies of foods and their constituent parts are being altered as they pass through factories where they may be subjected to crushing, high-speed machines, chemical treatment and excessive heat. These foreign abnormal resonances in food then may disrupt the normal energy balance of our tissues and meridians and this leads to a sequence of abnormal steps that can eventually kill us. Unfortunately, this can't be proven at this time.

This theory is consistent with current efforts to study different diets to see if they can heal. The common factor in all successful healing diets is the foods are all fresh and whole, no processed foods allowed. Therefore, it appears the best food for each individual would be the fresh foods to which his or her genetic ancestors adapted prepared as simply as possible.

The Anal Heater

The heater probe obviously delivers heat directly to the anus and blood passing through the area. Everyone agrees that heat enhances blood flow and this may help heal hemorrhoids and other local problems. Blood passing by the area will also be heated slightly and in most people core body temperatures may rise one degree F. I believe that when healing occurs in areas distant to the anus the heater is working more as a stimulator of the energy system described in Chinese Medicine.

Rodger once showed the anal heater to several other qigong masters. These qigong masters were unfamiliar with any stories of healing associated with the device yet they all predicted it should have great healing potential because of the relationship of the anus to the energy system.

From the perspective of body energies in TCM, the anus is located between two powerful energy points named Conception Vessel #1 and Governing Vessel #1. In the traditional medicine system of India (Ayurvedic medicine), Chakra #1 occupies the same location as Conception Vessel #1.

According to standard books on acupuncture, treatment of Conception Vessel #1 can be used to treat anuria (kidney failure

114

as in the case of Rodger's dog, Panda, described in Chapter 5), constipation, dysmenorrhea (as in the endometriosis case described in Anchorage in Chapter 4), hemorrhoids, and resuscitation of drowned persons. Governing Vessel #1 can be used to treat hemorrhoids, intestinal hemorrhage, diarrhea, vomiting, lumbar neuralgia and epilepsy.

Another concept of TCM is that treating one energy point on a meridian can produce an effect in other parts of the body over or through which the meridian passes. A headache may be treated successfully by needling an energy point on the foot that lies on the bladder meridian that passes over the top of the head. Effects also may be seen in tissues and organs traversed by other meridians that connect with the first as described in the basic theories of Traditional Chinese Medicine.

The Governing Vessel meridian begins at the tip of the coccyx (tail bone), progresses up the midline of the back, over the top of the head and ends in the middle of the upper lip. The Conception Vessel meridian begins in front of the anus, runs up the midline of the front of the body, and ends in the lower lip. Use of the heater in the mouth (with a new clean probe) stimulates both meridians and possibly more. When qigong master Hu used the anal heater in his mouth he said he could sense beneficial energy passing down the front of the chest to the heart. Also lying under the conception vessel meridian are the thymus gland and bone marrow in the sternum, both active participants in the immune system.

Another theory of action for the anal heater is that heat initiates a shock response in the body. This may cause a healing response, probably in the immune system and elsewhere. Shocking a person with heat or cold is an age-old practice in folk medicine around the world. This is why Rodger likes to use frozen balloons as a means of administering trace minerals in the rectum.

I would like to describe another way shock triggered healing responses in an experiment with salamanders conducted in 1962-3 at the Austrian Cancer Institute (as described in Robert Becker's book, *The Body Electric*). In that study salamanders

115

were painted with cancer causing chemicals until they developed cancer up and down the back and tail. Half the animals received routine care and died of cancer. Researchers cut off tails of the other animals making sure to cut through areas of the cancer. Those animals grew new tails as expected and as the tails grew back the cancers throughout the body shrank and disappeared completely. Please note that the cancer cells reverted back to normal cells and were not cut out or killed nor did they slough off.

The idea of being able to change cancer cells back to normal is foreign to concepts of western medicine. The prevailing approach is *the only good cancer cell is a dead cancer cell* and cancer cells must be *eradicated* (the common medical term) with treatments referred to among skeptics of orthodox medicine as *cutting, burning and poisoning.* I believe a better approach to treating cancer is to handle it the same way you would treat a son who got into trouble with the law. Most people wouldn't try to *eradicate* their son. Most would search for ways to slowly nudge his behavior back to normal.

Light and Pulsed Energy

Light can have powerful and unexpected effects. Light from the sun drives the photosynthesis that creates all of our food supply. Infrared rays from the sun warm our planet. It doesn't get more basic.

Light is used therapeutically as well. In medical school in the 1950s I saw premature babies placed under UV light in incubators to prevent brain damage from high levels of bilirubin in the blood (the result of immature livers). Strong lights are used to treat seasonal affective disorder (SAD), the depression associated with long dark winters in the north (a deficiency of light). Hot lasers are used in surgery. Other energy treatments are appearing as well, for example magnets, and ultrasound devices to promote healing of fractures.

It is becoming accepted that low level light therapy can relieve aches, pains and help in wound healing in addition to many

116

other applications. According to a computer search of the National Library of Medicine, there are over 1200 scientific articles on low level laser therapy (LLLT). Based on eighteen years of animal work and experiences in humans, LEDs pulsed at Nogier's frequencies appear to have far stronger healing effects than non-pulsed lasers set on low power outputs or non-pulsed LEDs regardless of their wavelengths (color).

Dan Parris offers an explanation of what may be happening when cells are treated with pulsed light, at least from the perspective of a physicist. He says atoms and molecules have resonance charges that affect their structure and it is possible for this resonance charge to be altered by such things as nutritional deficiencies and environmental factors. After a period of time the changes fix in place. He theorizes that intermittent treatment with pulsed light can retrain these delinquent atoms and molecules and get them to return to the structure and resonance they normally have.

Dan offers an analogy as a further explanation. If you strike a tuning fork that is caked with dried mud it will vibrate, but at a different frequency from normal. If the mud is fresh and wet (for example as in a new illness) the tuning fork can throw off the mud and return to normal resonance. Therefore, acute (short term) conditions are far easier to treat than chronic (long standing).

One question remains to be solved in the area of LEDs. In reading research on LLLT and LEDs a common statement is found that treatments must deliver a certain minimal quantity of light energy to be effective. If stimulating directly and accurately on energy points only 0.1 Joules is required. If stimulating an area of skin the minimum is 4 to 5 Joules per square centimeter surface area.

However, the energy delivered by the hand-held LED device designed by qigong master Hu delivers far less than that yet has more powerful healing effects and can be felt passing through lead. This characteristic fits the definition of qi (chi, ki, prana).

Theories of Traditional Chinese Medicine

I would like to give you a short overview of some of the theories of Traditional Chinese Medicine (TCM). TCM is very different in concept and practice from western medicine but from its history we can conclude it must have worked quite well. It is said that TCM doctors who treated the Emperor were killed if a treatment failed to help. Also, practitioners of TCM were paid on a routine basis to examine people and keep them well (a true concept of prevention) and if illness occurred the doctor had to treat for free. How many modern western doctors would agree to practice under these terms?

Doctors of TCM use several methods to diagnose the type of energy disturbance present. These include pulse diagnosis, history, tongue diagnosis and examination of stool and urine. Treatment methods include herbs (generally five or six selected from over 2,000 and boiled in a pot), acupuncture, moxa (heat), tuinah (massage), cupping, diet changes, qigong, tai chi (moving meditation of qigong) and a few others.

Most westerners are unaware that the energy system of the body has been recognized over and over as an indisputable fact by western scientific methods. Energy points are easily located on the skin because resistance to the passage of an electric current is reduced by 90% over the points. Over 600 energy points have been located by electronic testing and they all match the those found on ancient charts and dolls.

The energy points also show up on Kerlian photography (high voltage photography). In color videotapes of Kerlian photography energy points stand out like twinkling stars and are located exactly where described in old charts.

The meridians can also be demonstrated by injecting a radioisotope into energy points. The radioactive compound can be traced through the path of the meridian in the direction of flow shown in ancient charts. Studies were published in the 1960s in China, have been repeated in France and I have heard several

118

investigators have confirmed this work in Japan (see Appendix VI for references).

Even more remarkable is when these points were first described. Two thousand two hundred year old bronze dolls exist that were used to teach acupuncture to students. Energy points are represented as tiny holes in the surface of the dolls. During competence examinations the doll was covered with a thin layer of clay. The professor asked the trainee to place needles in holes representing energy points he selected and every time a needle missed a hole a deduction was made.

This raises the question of how the twelve paired energy meridians and 600 energy points were originally found. In China I was told some gifted people could see the system with a *sixth sense*, the same way some people can see auras of energy around others. Qigong master Hu says he can see the classical energy system but only when he is well rested.

One paradox in acupuncture and TCM may baffle the westerner unfamiliar with the subject. A person with diarrhea may be found to have *too much energy* in his Small Intestine meridian as opposed to a person with constipation who may have *too little energy* in the Small Intestine Meridian. The energy treatment to balance the disturbances could be the same for both, insertion of a needle into a specific energy point. The result may be that bowel function heads toward normal from the extremes.

This concept may explain why weight loss programs usually fail in America. A weight loss method may work for a while but if a normal pattern of energies in the body is not restored it will fail in the long run and this is what generally happens. Just look at all the things modern people do that are not best for their bodies. This would be my explanation of why Rodger's program appears to be successful in people trying to lose weight as well as other conditions and it has worked right in the face of a high fat diet of junk food.

Another aspect of TCM is very different. Western medicine frequently follows a practice of delaying treatment until a diagnosis is made. Often a special effort is required to cram patients'

119

symptoms and findings into some slot with a disease name on it so treatment can begin. Then the same treatment is mass applied to everyone with the same diagnosis. This certainly does not allow for individual differences in genetics, chemistry, diets, environments, activities, etc.

In contrast, doctors of TCM establish an energy related diagnosis and treat on that basis. Because of individual variations each person will be diagnosed with a different disturbance of the energy system and treatment is based on that individual pattern. This does not fit well into the current western system of computerized laboratory exams, MRIs, DRGs and insurance codes.

The Use of Multiple Modalities Together

Another reason we believe the program works is because of the synergistic effect of applying several steps simultaneously. This approach is the opposite of practices of western medicine that for the past 100 years have been locked into a model of one diagnosis-one treatment, for example, treating a strep throat infection with penicillin. Only recently have I heard western medical experts begin to say diseases may be caused by multiple factors.

I realize I give much of the credit for the success of Rodger's program to theories and practices of Chinese Medicine. If anyone can offer a better way of explaining what we are observing I would love to hear from them. Western medicine does a lot of observing and measuring but doesn't offer any viable theory of how our bodies really work.

As I write these words success is being announced in the genome project, the mapping of the human genetic code. Coincidently medicine is expanding efforts to produce genetically engineered solutions for diseases. All of this is amazing but lost in the excitement is the fact that nobody can explain how a DNA molecule works or why it should want to do more than just lie there sleeping in our chromosomes. A DNA strand is nothing more than a collection of chemicals bound together in the shape of a double helix (shaped like a spiral staircase). Understanding the mapping of sequences of millions of pairs of components of DNA is a far cry from knowing the secret of life, or even how DNA works.

The omission of energy concepts in western medicine causes problems in three ways. Sometimes energy medicine treatments may actually work better than anything offered by western medicine, as in acupuncture treatment for genital herpes. At other times effective energy based treatments may exist when western physicians believe they have none to offer at all. An important factor in these times is when energy based treatment is used as a substitute for western medicine costs go way down. Thus modern western medicine short-changes itself in several ways as it runs up huge medical bills.

As described the answer for many conditions and for prevention may be as simple as applying the methods described in this book and other similar low-tech inexpensive steps. To verify our observations and experiences all western experts need do is sink a bit of money into some simple equipment, conduct some fair trials, and see what happens. The only important question should be whether or not the program works and if it is safe. The answer to both questions appears to be a resounding yes.

Healing Energies of Heat and Light

CHAPTER 11: SLOW ACCEPTANCE OF NEW IDEAS IN MEDICINE

Throughout history every worthwhile new idea seems to be doomed to go through trying phases before being accepted. First it is ignored, then attacked as it gains popularity and challenges the status quo, and then embraced as if the majority accepted it from the start. The treatment approach described in this book may go through the same phases and if it does my hope is that the time period will be condensed. Linus Pauling once told me, "It is nice to be ahead of your time but only by about ten years. When people catch up to you they give you Nobel Prizes. If you are 30 years ahead of your time you will die unappreciated."

I would like to relate some classic tales of how new ideas have been suppressed in the field of medicine.

Western Medicine Has an Ugly History

An old expression in medicine says that new ideas are not accepted until the opposition dies off. To try to understand why medicine continues to act in this manner today you need to know its history. Prior to 300 years ago doctors were taught illnesses were caused by evil humors, spirits or swamp gas. Then things began to get a little more scientific but it didn't help patients very much.

William Harvey was personal physician to the King of England when he discovered the circulation of the blood in 1628 (actually, the Chinese made this discovery first in about 200 BC). Harvey knew blood was being pumped away from the heart through the arteries even though he had no ghost of an idea how the blood might be returned to the heart. He exposed arteries in the legs and arms of cadavers, drained blood and replaced it with water. He place colored liquid in the heart and squeezed the heart with his hand. With a few squeezes the colored liquid showed up in arteries in the feet and hands. You'd think this straightforward demonstration would convince skeptics but things don't work that way.

Instead of being frustrated in obscurity his connection with the King opened doors for him all over Europe where he had an opportunity to become frustrated out in the open. He traveled from one leading medical school to the next repeating his experiment on cadavers trying to convince professors of medicine that the heart really did pump blood to distant parts of the body. The top medical minds of the time saw the dye show up in the arteries of the feet and hands but walked away saying either they didn't see it or it didn't prove anything. The concept didn't fit into the dogmas of medicine of the time and was rejected for decades.

After the opposition died off the concept became accepted but medicine exaggerated its importance, developing it into a fad. Suddenly *all* illnesses were believed to be caused by abnormalities in the circulation of the blood. Every problem was henceforth classified as a blood circulation problem and there were supposed to be five types numbered I, II, III, IV, and V.

The new system had a major flaw. The numbering system may have sounded crystal clear at the time but nobody had a way to tell any difference between the five types of disorders. Doctors just put a finger up in the air to feel the breeze and picked one. In actuality, this failure to be able to distinguish one type from another didn't really make a difference. Treatment for all five disorders was almost identical and included blood letting and poisoning with some toxic material to drive the illness from the body. Type I disorder may call for blood letting and mercury purges. Type II may call for a good bleed plus arsenic. Type III would call for bloodletting plus a different toxin.

As an old man George Washington fell prey to this treatment when he developed some sort of infection in his throat and neck after being soaked in an ice storm. Over a three-day period he was drained of nine (yes 9) pints of blood (an average sized person only has twelve) and given mercury orally until he vomited and had diarrhea. Then for reasons his doctors couldn't understand he suddenly died.

Tom Paine wrote that George's doctors killed him with the treatment. Those were fighting words and the doctors defended their actions by suing Paine for slander. At trial the most highly respected medical educators in the country including Benjamin Rush, a signer of the declaration of independence, testified George received the highest quality of care known to mankind. Paine lost the case, couldn't pay damages and moved on to France in time to become involved in their revolution.

As crazy as bloodletting sounds to us today the fad dominated medical treatment for over 200 years. In the 1880s when bacteria were found to cause infections, blood letting vanished from the scene (very likely over a 30 year period as usual as elderly practitioners died off). There is no telling how many people died for no good reason.

Simmelweiss

In the 1850s obstetricians at the leading teaching hospital in Europe in Vienna, Austria, could not determine why 50% of all women delivering babies on their service died of infections. Along came Dr. Ignas Simmelweiss who discovered the death rate could be reduced drastically if physicians would simply wash their hands in a chlorine solution before deliveries.

Unfortunately for Simmelweiss and the patients he could offer no mechanism as a basis for his hypothesis so he was ignored. This duplicates a very modern approach in medicine in which new ideas are not accepted until a mechanism of action is discovered whereas old accepted treatments are not held to that lofty standard. In this case bacteria had been seen with powerful microscopes since the mid 1600s but nobody knew they could be the cause of infections until the late 1800s.

Medicine was coming into a golden age in Europe. It was a period of exploding knowledge as medicine was trying to convert itself into a scientific discipline (an attitude that continues today). Pathologists were autopsying anyone who died and in some areas of Austria autopsies were mandated by royal decree. Most of our familiar modern diseases were linked to pathologic findings and named during that time. At Simmelweiss' hospital obstetricians performed autopsies on their own patients who died hoping to advance knowledge in the new *scientific medicine.*

During these autopsies obstetricians literally dipped their bare hands into abdomens full of pus and wiped their hands off on filthy white lab coats. Considering the bacteria involved this meant their white coats were stained with mixes of colors from yellow to green and stunk to high heaven. Without washing their hands they proceeded back to the delivery ward and performed vaginal exams on women in labor and delivered babies. No one suspected these practices could lead to fatal infections. Simmelweiss was the first to suspect doctors may be transporting causative agents from the autopsy room to the labor and delivery suite. The very thought was repugnant to the highly trained and arrogant physicians whose belief system prevented them from looking at the problem objectively.

Across the hall from the doctor ward was a midwife delivery service. According to hospital rules (set by doctors) midwives were allowed to deliver babies but couldn't perform autopsies because their training was at a lower level than the physicians. The death rate from infection on their ward was only 1% and this was a constant source of irritation to the doctors. Physicians couldn't explain their horrible death rate while at the same time denying any causative role.

It was impossible to contain horror stories told by women who survived deliveries on the doctors' ward and over time word spread about the huge number of deaths. Upon entry to the hospital women in labor were arbitrarily assigned to either the midwife ward or the doctor ward. Things got so bad women in labor were refusing admission to the doctor ward and fled from the hospital to deliver their babies on the street. This vastly improved their chances of surviving childbirth but further irritated the obstetricians.

Over the years Simmelweiss worked his way up the academic ladder until he was second in command on the obstetrics service. The golden opportunity to test his hypothesis came when his chief of service went on sabbatical to England for three months leaving him in charge. He immediately placed strict rules into effect requiring resident physicians to wash their hands before entering the labor and delivery suite. The young doctors thought these regulations were ridiculous and obeyed them only when forced to do so.

Simmelweiss found he had to remain at the entry door to the labor and delivery suite to ensure that the trainees washed their hands in a basin of chlorine water before entering. He remained there 24 hours a day and as long as he stayed awake there were few deaths. When he fell asleep the resident physicians passed by the washbasin and infection related deaths returned. Even with these lapses the overall death rate fell dramatically during those three months, frequently approaching zero. However, when the chief of service returned and discovered what was happening he fired Simmelweiss.

For the next 30 years Simmelweiss tried to convince obstetricians to wash their hands with no success. He finally went crazy and died in a mental hospital.

Shortly after his death bacteria were identified as causative agents in infections. At long last a mechanism of action was discovered that explained the spread of infection from the autopsy room to the living. Almost overnight Simmelweiss was recognized as a great man, a man far ahead of his time. Many hospitals on the continent still bear his name. This is a good example of how physicians throughout history stubbornly refuse to accept a new advance until someone can prove how it works, or enough time passes for the opposition to die off.

The Germ Theory of Disease

With the discovery of bacteria as the cause of infection doctors no longer diagnosed blood circulation disorders I through V or bled people to death. All that was ridiculed but never with self-critical comments about how stupid they had been to practice blood letting for over 200 years. The new fad belief was that all diseases were caused by bacterial infection. This approach is called the *germ theory of disease* and we are only now passing out of this phase as medicine moves on into expensive genetic manipulations and other high tech solutions that sound wonderful (and expensive) on the evening news.

The germ theory really solidified in the 1930s and 1940s when antibiotics appeared on the scene. This led to the concept of *one cause-one treatment* in medicine, hardly a holistic or ecologic idea. An example of this is the treatment of a strep throat infection with penicillin. Medicine only now is beginning to consider how a multitude of environmental factors may interact with individual genetic patterns to cause diseases. However, any theory of subtle energy disturbances in the body does not fit into this paradigm. No theories are being advanced to explain how our bodies work through a complicated system of switches that are being turned on and off continuously.

Linus Pauling PhD

Linus Pauling PhD is the only person to win two Nobel prizes individually. He received his first Nobel Prize for discovering the genetic and chemical nature of sickle-cell anemia and this opened up the entire new area of what medicine calls *molecular diseases*. The second Nobel Prize was for peace. Pauling calculated how many excess cancer deaths would occur because of atmospheric testing of atomic weapons in the 1940s and 1950s. After gathering his facts he embarked on a worldwide speaking tour trying to convince people and governments to ban the dangerous practice.

This infuriated officials in Washington DC who viewed future atmospheric testing as being vital to our national defense. Our State Department called him a communist (the worst way to blast a person at the time) and took away his passport. This prevented Dr. Pauling from traveling to England to attend a scientific meeting where an electron microscopic photo of a DNA molecule on end was presented for the first time.

Pauling had previously discovered that DNA had a helix (spiral) shape but couldn't pin down if it was a single, double, or triple helix. This photo supplied the missing link in the puzzle. Watson and Crick pieced the information together, proved DNA was a double helix, and won a Nobel Prize. Pauling came that close to being awarded his third individual Nobel Prize and may have done so but for the insane action of our government.

In later years Pauling took an interest in vitamin C after reading a book by biochemist Irving Stone PhD. Whenever he decided to investigate a subject he was very thorough and asked his secretary to pull every scientific reference on the subject. He read *all* the scientific literature about vitamin C (possibly the only one who has ever read the thousands upon thousands of articles) and concluded the vitamin had many useful functions when taken at doses much higher than the RDA. By the time he died at age 93 he himself was taking 22,000 mg. a day in many divided doses.

Medical doctors were outraged at what he was saying about vitamin C and its relationship to the common cold. They said he was invading their turf (Pauling didn't have an MD) and because he spoke very slowly and deliberately detractors said he was going senile.

I met Dr. Pauling on several occasions and once had dinner with him. I found him to be a down to earth friendly fellow and after that night he would pick me out of a crowd at a meeting, come over, shake my hand and greet me by name. He did speak in a slow deliberate way but I think this was because he was forced to choose his words carefully because someone was likely to overhear a conversation and quote him.

It was Pauling who made me see the fallacy of the cholesterol theory. At that time (1970s) I had been brainwashed into thinking eggs were poison and beef should disappear from the planet. Pauling told me that if the body is well nourished in all of the nutrients it needs to function normally then the fat and cholesterol issues will take care of themselves and not present a problem. After all, we are omnivores and in medical school were taught that our bodies have the chemistry to handle all kinds of foods. Then heart attacks appeared on the scene (the first heart attack ever documented by autopsy in the world occurred in 1878). Blame had to be placed somewhere and saturated fat and cholesterol were the first to be associated with the disease if only in the weakest of ways.

Pauling once made a statement I remember well. When asked why other scientists did not agree with his opinions his answer was, "Ignorance of the facts."

Summary

Human beings seem to resist change in every way and medicine is no exception. Throughout the history of medicine new ideas have been met with resistance and ridicule. The pattern continues today even though physicians deny this, saying we have gotten so smart and have learned from mistakes of the past. The exception may be the acceptance of a technology that makes new surgical procedures possible (surgeons strongly believe in surgery) or a new drug with an extensive advertising budget.

However, things are changing in medicine very rapidly in two ways. About half of the population is beginning to use alternative approaches of some kind. This is forcing conventional physicians to inform themselves about alternative treatments at least to learn about what their patients may be doing. What they may learn is that many approaches they have automatically rejected in the past actually may work and fit into the medicine of the future. In addition the high and perpetually rising cost of health care is forcing HMOs and insurance plans to look for ways to deliver adequate levels of services for less money. They may be forced to take these steps over the loud opposition of physicians.

Rodger and I hope that given this climate and rapid worldwide communication made possible by the Internet the program described in this book will receive a fair evaluation and not be routinely rejected automatically as in the past.

CHAPTER 12: FREQUENTLY ASKED QUESTIONS

1. Why should anyone believe you?

In the beginning I had a hard time believing all of this was true myself, even with a background of 26 years in alternative medicine plus qigong. Then I saw people with all kinds of ailments getting better, reviewed the medical records of some of the sickest and came out of retirement to get involved.

I expect the majority of people who hear about this program will reject it for many years to come. That is how the human mind treats new breakthroughs.

2. Are any of the treatments harmful?

The treatments are very safe but there is some possibility of harm in three areas. Debilitated people could become dehydrated in the sauna but that has always been a danger with saunas. It certainly is not wise to enter the sauna when a niacin flush is in full bloom as this will increase the possibility of a blood pressure drop from the combined effect of dehydration and pooling of blood in the skin.

A second area of concern is there may be people who may try to copy this program who don't understand the risk of overdosing when minerals are given in the rectum. Supplementing minerals by the rectal route is tricky. When minerals are taken orally they don't just all pour into the blood. The small intestine decides how much of each mineral will be absorbed into the blood. Specific absorption mechanisms exist for each trace mineral that guard against absorbing too much and a possible overdose. The same mechanisms allow larger than normal amounts to be absorbed if the body needs more at that time.

An example commonly used is the trace mineral zinc where the oral Daily Value for elemental zinc is 15 mg but only about 1 mg is absorbed, an optimal amount. This 1 mg dose is also the typical daily dose of zinc given intravenously to people who can't take any nourishment orally (people forced to be on

131

TPN, or total parenteral nutrition). Giving the full oral Daily Value dose of 15 mg either in the vein or rectally could result in a severe overdose, even death.

Another problem can arise when people don't use common sense. They may try this program when it may not be the best thing to do at the time, such as getting an appendix removed when they develop appendicitis.

3. Can you overdose on the LED blanket?

We don't believe so. In over one year of experience with prototype instruments this has not been reported.

4. Where can these devices and materials be purchased?
See *Resources* in the appendix.

5. Is this an expensive regime?

There are upfront expenses that won't be covered by insurance. However, if you consider what the devices may do (those manufactured by Chee Energy), that they will last for years and the entire family can use them over and over, they are a bargain. Also, all of the devices described are sold on a money back basis within a reasonable time, if a purchaser wishes to return them for any reason.

6. Doesn't this program sound like a cure-all that can't be real?

Yes! It sounds like one because it appears to stimulate a healing response at such a basic level it might be possible to have a beneficial effect on any condition. People researching LLLT have mentioned this as a problem in the acceptance of their work because most scientists are not familiar with approaches that work in a widespread way.

We don't yet know the limits of the program because of limited experience. Certainly this program is not going to replace surgery for appendicitis, cancer, birth defects, trauma and many other problems, or the use of antibiotics in life saving situations.

7. What do you think of the borderline at which medicine declares someone to have a condition that is hopeless?

Not much. For the 26 years I have been involved in alternative medicine I have heard of and seen many recoveries after conventional physicians wrote off people as being hopeless. Hank is a perfect example (Chapter 3).

8. If I try this program should I discontinue seeing my doctor or stop following his or her advice?

Certainly not. We advise continuing whatever treatment you are following and adding on this program. There may be disease conditions where you will need to work closely with your doctor, such as in diabetes with the use of insulin. Rodger's dad, Hank, has worked closely with his cardiologist through the years. Many drugs have dangerous side effects when they are stopped suddenly and you may need the help of a physician to guide you in trying to reduce doses. We believe everyone should maintain a good relationship with a doctor and this is most important if and when an emergency arises.

9. Where do you see medicine going in the future?

For years orthodox-dominated research committees have not approved funding to explore radically new ideas. The NIH (National Institutes of Health) now has an office of alternative medicine that in 2000 has a research budget of 68 million dollars per year. Alternative medicine gets good press coverage now (compared to being attacked on evening network news shows 20 years ago) and courses for medical students are offered in the majority of our medical schools. Even qigong is receiving attention. Ken Sancier of the Qigong Institute tells me research in qigong is currently being conducted at the University of Michigan and the University of Arizona. This was unheard of ten years ago.

The driving force for funding research in this area comes from an odd source. Alternative medicine has touched the lives of a few congressmen (including one former congressman whose hopeless cancer went away with alternative medicine) and they have gone to bat for the approach.

Many changes have occurred in medicine since I first studied acupuncture in 1974 and the speed of change is accelerating. As many have said previously, medicine of the future will include a large list of options (more than simply drugs and surgery) and will provide a mixture of treatments that work the best and are the most cost effective and risk free. Ideally treatment methods should be allowed to compete on their merits without interference from multibillion-dollar multinational drug companies that do anything they can to influence how medicine is practiced and to fatten their bottom lines. I believe in the future many current high-tech procedures of medicine will become obsolete or too expensive for the small benefits they may bring.

10. A wonderful product cured my problem. Can I send you a sample?

We know there are many fine products out there that have helped people. However, what may work well for one person may not work for 95% of the rest of us. We have tried to keep our focus very narrow and simple from the beginning. Rodger screened literally thousands of products over several years but selected only a few because of special energetic properties he could sense with his body. The main thing about the methods he selected is they work in almost everyone.

We are not looking for more products but if you wish to send something to be tested feel free to do so. I can ask Rodger to screen the material with his energy-sensing hands. If it feels good to him he will try it on himself, always his first step. This sets the bar at a very high level and few products or approaches will pass.

11. If I get better using this program, when can I stop?

I like to use an analogy offered by my friend Tris Trethart MD of Edmonton, Canada. If you eat a meal and feel full does this mean you can stop eating forever? We live in a polluted world where our subtle energies are bombarded constantly with negative inputs of all types. It pays to try to maintain a normal energy balance and we believe this can be accomplished with this program but it must be continued indefinitely to serve well as a preventive.

12. You have described several instruments and treatments. Which ones do we really need to buy?

The essential minimum would be an LED blanket, anal heater and a continuing supply of special minerals and supplements. The sauna is also very helpful and Rodger promises to find a way to deliver an inexpensive version.

13. Which blanket should I buy, the all red or more expensive red, white and blue?

Blankets composed entirely of red LEDs have been on the market for about four years, have a good healing record and those were the first ones Rodger bought and used. Before development of the multicolored LED blanket I found that two women working to recover from paralysis of an arm could move their arms better when the red LED blanket was turned on than when off (done so they couldn't see if the blanket was on or off). Therefore, the red blanket does work. The question is how well.

Almost everyone using the red, white and blue blanket reports feeling energy tingling through the body and almost nobody has this experience with the red blanket. When Rodger treats his most energy-sensitive clients with both blankets (one after the other in the same treatment) they feel more things happening in the body with the multicolored blanket.

Qigong master Hu designed the red, white and blue blanket as an improvement on the all red blanket after I asked him how we could streamline the program. Hu told us the all red blanket had a healing power of 50% of qi whereas the red, white and blue blanket elevated this to 90%. Now, after using the blanket for six months, Rodger has concluded the multicolored blanket does work better for most but not everyone.

14. You once were skeptical of the theories of TCM. What do you think of them now?

Over the past 13 years I have seen many qigong masters in action but they never provided a clear description of what they observed in the energy field of a patient using their *sixth sense* or why they approached a problem a specific way. The only thing they told us was that they were working to clear energy blocks and imbalances.

Then I had the opportunity to watch qigong master Hu in action. Hu held back nothing, gave me a running account of the energy disturbances he was seeing, and why he was doing what he was doing. He treated everyone differently but always followed what flowed according to the strange sounding theories of Chinese Medicine. The impressive thing was that his treatments always worked.

When this working relationship developed I got out my old books and reviewed the theories of Chinese Medicine so I could ask Hu more informed questions. After this experience I now believe the theories of Chinese Medicine completely because I have seen them work so well. Why they work still remains a mystery.

15. Qigong masters sound powerful and scary. Have any qigong masters ever abused their powers?

I once asked Dr. Kong this question in China. He said he heard of one qigong master who used his abilities to play practical jokes on people he didn't like. Without warning he lost all of his powers as if they were lifted from him by a higher power.

16. How can shining a light of weak energy on the skin change anything inside the body?

Nobody knows but you should consider this: premature babies with immature livers have been treated with ultraviolet light to prevent permanent brain damage from excessive bilirubin levels for over 50 years. Diapers are removed, the eyes covered and the organ treated is the skin. The mechanism of action for that treatment remains unknown but doctors don't question it because in medical school they are taught it works and they can see it work.

17. How many treatment failures have you heard of with the program described?

As of the date of writing this book (July 2000) I know of only a small number of outright treatment failures with the program. Everyone who has used the complete program for a reasonable time has improved to some extent and many became completely well, even those with serious conditions considered to be irreversible by physicians. There have also been successes among people who used only that part of the program as it was in development, for example using the sauna and anal heater without the minerals and LEDs.

18. How does this overall regime work?

I wish I knew. What I can say is that the healing effect seems to be working at a basic level, possibly the level of molecules or atoms in cells, maybe even at the sub-atomic level. Why the use of these modalities in combination produces synergistic healing remains a mystery.

19. Do you really believe these new LED devices emit true chi?

That's a trick question because nobody has identified chi through scientific means or any other. Therefore it is impossible to say something is exactly the same as chi when there is no known standard of comparison. Even qigong master Hu warned us we were healing with light, not qi, and the energy of qi was different and on a higher level.

However, the energy emitted by the *X-Light* instrument comes close to passing the "duck" test. It produces effects at a distance, it can be felt passing through lead and it can speed healing in the skin where it is plain to see. These are some of the characteristics of the mysterious chi, our life force energy. Qigong masters tell us the instrument emits an energy very *similar* to chi. This is the reason we say it produces energy that is different and more effective than energy from LLLT or other LED devices.

20. Is there a way to show these new LED devices can balance meridian stress?

Yes. Modern electronic devices pattered after earlier devices of Reinhold Voll MD of Germany take readings on meridians and can identify those that are out of balance or experiencing stress. Doctors who work with this equipment say they have seen abnormal readings return to normal following treatment for one to two minutes with the *X-Light*. This provides a form of objective proof. We invite others trained in the use of these types of testing devices to try out both the *X-Light* and the multi-colored blanket and inform us of their experiences.

21. I have an aversion to putting anything into my anus and treat that area as a one-way valve. Do I really need to use the anal heater and rectal trace minerals?

During early development of the program Rodger was freezing minerals in distilled water in balloons, having people slit the end of the balloon and insert the frozen suppository through the anus. Then we found many people had clairvoyant anuses that went into spasm when the frozen suppository approached, even when it was inches away. A compromise was made in the use of room temperature distilled water in a Fleets bottle.

Later another compromise developed allowing the liquid trace minerals to be given under the tongue or in juice. Many people find this to be a far more comfortable experience. Rodger continues to believe the rectal route is more effective.

Omitting use of the anal heater is a different issue. Because the program works through some synergistic interaction in the energy system failure to use the anal heater might just mean the difference between success and failure of the program.

SUMMARY

I believe you will agree this has been a wild unpredictable ride. Nobody ever dreamed that synergistic healing responses could ever flow from the use of a few simple treatment modalities that are available without doctors or prescriptions, not even Rodger himself. It was amazing how, during a period of about nine months, one idea after another came to us, almost as if we were being spoon-fed information at just about the fastest rate we could absorb without out brains exploding. Every time we needed something or had a problem the solution seemed to fall into our laps as if it were meant to happen. We will leave philosophizing on that topic to others.

After observing seemingly impossible healing responses we tried to explain *why* this combination of therapies worked so well. Gradually it became apparent most of the results could be explained through the theories and concepts of Chinese Medicine though I had resisted becoming a total convert to those strange sounding theories for 26 years.

The best part of the program is it offers a powerful new way for individuals to balance their energy systems in the privacy of their own homes. Our bodies have potent built-in healing systems that are seldom used because they are suppressed by negative factors in the modern world such as contaminated water, air, stress and processed foods. At long last we may have a simple way to activate these latent healing abilities through do-it-yourself methods.

It has been my pleasure to bring this information to you. I hope you have the opportunity to try the program and see what it may do for you.

APPENDIX I: HOW TO USE THESE NEW MODALITIES

Before providing you with instructions on how to use this program I would like to review some basic principles.

1. It is wise to practice good health habits at all the times but most of us don't. The nutritional quality of our food plays a huge role in our current pattern of disease. In veterinary practice it is commonly accepted that a treatment may not work or an animal can't become pregnant until nutrients are pumped in. This applies to humans as well. Therefore, please try to ignore the temptations of modern foods and eat fresh whole foods.

2. The more severe the health situation the longer the program will need to be followed without deviation to see if it is going to work. A trial period of up to three months may be required in some cases, enough time for the body to begin to rebuild normal tissues.

3. As above, the more severe the condition the more important it becomes to use all modalities described within a twelve-hour period. It is unlikely you will solve a severe problem by using just one or two approaches and omitting the remainder.

4. Through the combined experimental studies of Rodger, qigong master Hu and various veterinarians, different treatment schedules have been developed for different symptoms and illnesses. These are not written in stone and are subject to change in the future. Basically, people with serious illnesses need treatments more often with longer exposure times to the LEDs. People who are moderately ill (the walking wounded) are advised to take treatments twice a week using all of the modalities on the same day. If used on a preventive basis the program can be reduced to using all modalities on the same day, once a week.

5. Remember, you must re-learn to love yourself, feel good about yourself and be willing to take some time to do something good for yourself. This should not cause guilt because you are taking *so-called* valuable time from something you may incorrectly believe is more important.

In summary a typical single treatment session using all modalities on the same day would be as follows:

1. Take the trace minerals (tiny doses) either under the tongue or rectally and drink a dose of the vitamin C, niacin, and ribose powder. This should produce a *niacin flush* that facilitates the circulation of other nutrients more thoroughly throughout your tissues.
2. Wait until the niacin flush has passed before proceeding on (usually a minimum of 30 minutes). This pause is important for safety reasons to prevent dehydration and a possible drop in blood pressure with fainting.
3. Take a 30-minute infrared sauna taking care to drink lots of water or juice to prevent dehydration.
4. Following the sauna use the LED blanket for 10 to 15 minutes.
5. Take a 10 to 15 minute treatment with the anal heater. This can be combined with the use of the LED blanket.

More specific instructions are as follows:

Nutrients:

The product called ***Formula #1*** contains tiny doses of trace minerals that can be taken either as sublingual drops or rectally. Rodger prefers the rectal route. If you are going to use the liquid trace minerals orally place the dose advised under the tongue (away from food) and hold there for three or four minutes before swallowing the remainder.

142

If using the product rectally empty a Fleets Enema bottle, wash it out with soap and water and rinse at least five times. Fill the bottle half full with distilled water and add the liquid minerals to the water according to the dosage indicated on the bottle. Do not exceed this dose. Insert this liquid solution into the rectum.

Take one level teaspoon of the **Royal Flush** powder dissolved in a half glass of liquid. The oral powder contains 50 mg of niacin, enough to give most people a *niacin flush*. This is a harmless, tingly, prickly, flushing with redness all over the body (sometimes very uncomfortable) that lasts about 20 to 30 minutes. The flush will enhance circulation of nutrients throughout the body. If no flushing occurs with the recommended dose add an additional 50 mg of niacin to your next treatment, preferably in powder form. This can be purchased separately at health food stores. Do not use the enteric-coated timed-release form of niacin because it has been associated with liver toxicity. Don't take the flushing dose and then do something else that will cause you to sweat or lose body fluids as dehydration could occur.

If you don't experience a flush with the increased dose (100 mg of niacin) gradually increase the dose of niacin with each treatment by 50 mg. until you achieve a good flush, then continue with that dose on treatment days. These oral and rectal nutrients should generally be used no more than twice a week. Be certain to allow the niacin flush to clear completely before proceeding to the next step.

Infrared sauna:

If one is available take a 30-minute infrared sauna any time after the niacin flush has passed. This waiting period is important in order to prevent a drop in blood pressure caused by flushing and sweating at the same time.

An infrared sauna can be an expensive item but you may be able to share one with a friend, talk a health club into purchasing one, or buy a small portable model (See page 167).

Possible side effects:

Dehydration is the biggest worry. Guard against this by drinking plenty of fluids during the sauna, generally two large glasses full. If you begin to feel weak or lightheaded open the door, get out, sit down or lie down and drink more liquids.

This step (if a sauna is available) should be done no more than twice a week and on the same days as the rectal nutrients and anal heater are used.

Blankets of pulsed LED lights

Two patterns of pulsed LED blankets are available, one containing red and infrared LEDs (the ***Red-Carpet***) and one containing red, white, blue and infrared diodes (the ***Energy-Balancer***). If at all possible it is best to not put a lot of weight directly on these blankets, especially using them on hard surfaces. Such use increases the possibility of breaking solder joints connecting LEDs even though they are mounted in protective plates. This can cause short circuits and failure of segments of lights.

Either lie on your stomach on the floor or on a bed with the blanket on your back, or sit with it on your back in a recliner chair. With the blanket on the back the middle row of LEDs should line up with the midline of the body and the top of the blanket should be around the base of the skull. When the blanket is on the chest Master Hu advised not placing it higher than the notch of the neck. Since then Rodger has found this makes no difference and covers the head and neck with blankets.

When the LEDs are first turned on (with products of *Chee Energy*) they will automatically cycle through seven pulsed frequencies discovered by Dr. Paul Nogier. Individual frequencies also can be selected for treatment. In the ***Energy-Balancer*** blanket the user also has the option of choosing from three color patterns: 1) red, white, blue, infrared, 2) red and infrared, 3) blue.

If no symptoms exist and you are using the system for preventive purposes use the blanket for ten minutes on the front of the chest and ten minutes on the back (as described) twice per week. Using the blanket in the evening while watching TV is a convenient way to do this and not disrupt your normal routine. The LED blanket can also be used at the same time as the anal heater to save time.

If only moderately ill (the walking wounded) use the blanket for fifteen minutes on each side (front and back) twice per week. If the problem clears completely you may be able to reduce exposure time to ten minutes on each side.

If you are seriously ill (such as with cancer, stroke, or diabetes with insulin use) use the blanket for 20 to 30 minutes on the front and back every day for the first 15 days. Then, gradually reduce exposure time as symptoms decrease. This may require monitoring by a health professional.

As an extra energy-balancing bonus after using the blanket treat the tips of the fingers and toes with the hand held device (the *X-Light*, see below) on the frequency E setting. Aim the small cluster of LEDs at the tips of the fingers of one hand from a distance of about three to four inches for one minute and repeat this step on the other hand and both feet for one minute each.

Please read information at the end of this chapter for a list of the possible contraindications of LED therapy.

You may wish to try a method of use I like to follow. Take the liquid minerals and oral powder and lie in bed with the LED blanket on the chest with the anal heater in place for 10 to 15 minutes. With covers pulled up high the niacin flush kicks in and you feel relaxed and warm. Most people feel energy moving in the body as a tingling and say it is difficult to stay awake. After the flush clears take a 30-minute infrared sauna.

Please see the color photo section for a picture of the *Energy-Balancer* blanket.

145

A Hand-held LED Instrument (the *X-Light*)

This instrument is our favorite, the first prototype instrument qigong master Hu could hold in his hand and test on his sensitive energy system. The instrument now (2003) consists of an oval box slightly larger than a pack of cigarettes with three triangular patterns of red, white, and blue LEDs plus two infrared LEDs. A switching mechanism allows the user to choose between three color patterns: 1) red, white, blue, and infrared, 2) red and infrared, and 3) blue.

Researchers in LLLT and LED treatment say it takes 0.1 Joule to stimulate an energy point and a minimum of 4 to 5 Joules per square centimeter of skin surface to begin to see a biologic effect in tissues (a Joule is one watt-second). This hand-held instrument can produce beneficial effects within seconds when held three to four inches away and therefore must be working some other way. The energy can be felt passing through the body, through lead, and from greater distances. This fits the description of *chi* itself and qigong masters have told us the device emits energy very similar to the elusive *chi*.

We have had more opportunity to test this instrument than any other. I began carrying one of the prototypes in my shirt pocket and searched for people who had just suffered a bump, scratch, or other minor injury. I aimed the instrument at the injury for a minute or two and the pain usually went away. Many people told me what happened reminded them of how the fictional physician called "Bones" treated patients on the TV show *Star Trek*.

The instrument may be used on setting A for a minute or two to treat skin lesions, birth marks, hemangiomas (blood vessel clusters in the skin), scars, cuts, bruises and burns. In the case of burns it is beneficial to have an instrument handy because the LEDs must be applied within minutes to prevent blistering. Once you begin to use the instrument you will discover its many uses and want to keep it in your pocket or purse.

Once you have an *X-Light* in your hands try it out on friends. Select frequency E and slowly circle light from the LEDs around the edges of the palm and ask if they feel anything. Energy sensitive individuals will feel something instantly. Even most skeptics will be surprised and forced to admit they feel a cool breeze, tingling, or warmth where the light is hitting the skin. If warmth is experienced ask them to touch the LEDs and discover they remain cool.

Aim the instrument on the E frequency for one or two minutes at the clustered fingernails of people who feel energies easily. Many will report they feel an energetic tingling in the part of their body in which they are having a problem.

If meridian stress assessment equipment is available have readings taken on your meridians. Treat the energy points with abnormal readings for a minute or two on frequency E (with full color panel) and repeat the readings. Usually the readings will be corrected instantly.

The instrument is also powerful enough to be used to treat energy disturbances in organs and tissues in the body. You can use two sources of information to find an appropriate frequency. First look in Appendix II, *Embryologic Origin of Tissues*. If treating an organ select the frequency that matches the embryologic origin of the tissue (A, B, or C). If treating a specific condition look in the list at the end of this Appendix and treat the affected area with the frequency listed for ten minutes.

Red and blue colors can be used to affect mood balance. Red stimulates and may help symptoms of fatigue, feeling sluggish, depression, low sex drive, pessimism, and having little interest in life. Blue may help symptoms of anxiety, hot temper, trouble sleeping, impulsive behavior, being easily stressed, being overly active but tiring easily, and lack of staying power..

The Anal Heater—*(Now the Delwa Star H+P ™)*

No more than twice a week follow the above with a ten to fifteen-minute anal heater treatment. Turn up the heat to the highest setting you can tolerate with comfort. Many people begin with a temperature setting of 104-105° F and after a few minutes are able to slowly move the dial up to the maximum of 113 F°. Nothing is gained by trying to turn up the heat to an uncomfortable level.

For preventive purposes use it once a week for ten to fifteen minutes. This has been shown to reduce the incidence and severity of colds and flus during winter months most likely by stimulating better function of the immune system. With the first symptoms of a head cold take a 10-minute treatment. About 80% of the time the cold is all gone in a few hours!

The recommended pattern of use is different for hemorrhoids than for prostate enlargement symptoms or prostatitis. With hemorrhoids recommended use is 20 minutes twice a day for a few days, then again with recurrences. For prostate symptoms most men start by using the device several days in a row, then they reduce use to once or twice a week. We believe that with continued use day after day the immune system may adapt to the treatment and stop responding.

On each of the two days before any scheduled surgery use the anal heater once for 40 minutes. Use the device every other day following surgery for 20 minutes until healed. This has been shown to help control bleeding during surgery, reduce swelling and speed healing afterward.

If for some reason you are unable to use the heater in the anus or if the anus has been surgically removed, you can use the heater in the mouth for 15 to 20 minutes twice a week when ill and once a week for prevention. You can place the metal probe either under or on the tongue and use a low temperature setting. For other than anal uses a spare, clean probe may be purchased, marked for identification and stored separately (in a labeled plastic bay). Another option is to clean the probe thoroughly with rubbing alcohol, or soap and water, cover it in a plastic wrap (such as Saran Wrap), and use it in body openings in the head.

For tinnitus (ringing in the ears) use the metal probe in the offending ear for 15 minutes twice a week on a low setting.

For ear infections in children use the probe in the offending ear for 15 minutes twice a day on a low setting along with other more conventional treatments.

For heart problems use the metal probe in the mouth on a low setting for fifteen minutes twice a week.

Try the heater at bedtime if you have insomnia. Many people use the heater at bedtime and fall asleep with it turned on. Some do this intentionally by taping the cord to the leg. The probe will cool when the battery runs low and this does damage the battery.

Lubricating the aluminum tip with a little K-Y or petroleum jelly will make insertion in the anus easier. The tip is only two inches long and has an indentation the anal sphincter (muscle) can grab to hold in place. There is no need to insert the probe any further even if you are treating a prostate condition (the tip of the probe does not need to touch the prostate to provide benefit in prostate conditions). Newer units feature a 3" long prostate probe.

A dial (rheostat) on the unit controls the temperature of the tip. At a top setting of 113° the tip will heat to a maximum of 113° F. This temperature is far below the 130° F required to cause injury to tissue inside the rectum.

This Pattern can be Altered

The above patterns of use are subject to alteration. For example, in Rodger's experiences of 1999-2000 two people with colon cancer with metastases to the liver were being seen at the same time. One used all of the methods in the program twice a week at Rodger's home. Fifteen metastases in the liver disappeared within five months and fourteen months after beginning the program he is cancer free.

The other gentleman was able to take only a small number of saunas and couldn't use the heater in the anus because of pain caused by previous X-ray treatment. That gentleman took the powder mix and used the *X-Light* for 20 minutes over each tumor area daily (on E), seven days a week. His downhill course was arrested, all of his symptoms cleared and he began to gain real body weight even though his tumor continued to grow and his overall prognosis remained poor (Chapter 4).

I have a treatment plan in mind for myself if I ever develop cancer. I am not offering this as medical advice for others and it should not be taken that way or influence personal decisions of people with cancer.

I would have surgery if the tumor could be removed and would consider additional treatments offered by orthodox medicine if convincing evidence exists they might work and side effects would not be devastating. Then I would use all the modalities in this program twice a week increasing the frequency of the ribose/vitamin C/niacin powder mix to three days a week. I would treat myself over the tumor area with the *X-Light* set on frequency E for 20 minutes every day. I also would use the *Energy-Balancer* blanket two hours a day, one hour on each side. I also would remain open to any other non-toxic treatments that made sense after investigation.

Use All the Modalities Together

I would like to stress the importance of using all of these modalities together on one day. No one can explain why combining these simple steps promotes a synergistic effect but this is what we have observed over and over and this is what makes this program stand out and worthy of investigating. We believe use of the same modalities in a random scattered pattern will not produce the same level of healing responses.

List of Conditions and Treatment Frequencies According to Experiences of Veterinarians Since 1982

This list was developed over many years and represents the pooled experience of scores of veterinary acupuncturists who have used LED instruments with Nogier's frequencies on animals. It is provided as a guide to treatment of local problems.

General energy balancing steps should be taken first by treating with a blanket of LEDs that can be used either with automatic cycling of frequencies or set on one frequency that matches an organ or problem. Then pass the *X-Light* over a troublesome area using the frequency listed below for two to three minutes.

Arthritis - E
Back problems - E, C, or B
Bone problems - C
Bone chips - E
Chronic conditions not responsive to frequencies A or C, use
      D
Circulation, to increase after acute stage - F
Circulatory problems in general -   B
Ectodermal origin tissue, to treat use - A
    (body openings, skin, nerves, eye)
Edema - G or B
Endodermal origin tissue - B
    (circulation tissue [arteries, veins, lung, lymph system},
    GI tract, liver, pancreas)
Endocrine (hormone) problems - F
Eye, corneal ulcers - A
Eye injuries - A
Fractures, non-healing - F
Inflammation, to reduce in infections and injuries - G
Ligaments – C
Liver -- B
Lymphatic problems (water retention, edema) - B
Mesodermal origin tissue (bones, ligaments, lung, liver,
    tendons, muscles) - C
Mouth, gums - A or G
Muscle spasms - C
Nerve tissue - A

151

Pain (anywhere, any source) – E
Prostate – B and C
Skin - A
Surgery post-op - A
Tendon - C
Universal Frequencies - G or A (Universal frequencies can
be used when a treatment frequency is unknown).

Uses of color patterns with LEDs

You may benefit from red light therapy if you have any of the
following symptoms:

- Excessive fatigue
- Feeling "down," pessimistic
- Low sex drive
- Difficulty getting up in AM
- Disorganized
- Little interest in life

You may benefit from blue light therapy if you have the following
symptoms:

- Anxiety
- Hot temper
- Impulsive behavior
- Trouble sleeping
- Easily stressed
- Excessive activity, but tire easily
- Lack of staying power

Because of biochemical individuality you may need to experiment
on yourself to find patterns of use that you find of value while not
aggravating symptoms.

Possible contraindications to the use of LEDs.

Although there are no definite contraindications to using
LEDs, people with certain medical conditions might be wise to

avoid using them just to err on the side of caution including those who are sensitive to light. Pekka Pontinen PhD, MD, created this super-cautious list:

1. People with pacemakers.
2. Women who are pregnant.
3. Avoid treating the long bone joints of children who are still growing. (The fear is bone growth might be slowed.)
4. Avoid using LEDs over the thyroid gland. (Rodger does this all the time and people get better, not worse. Qigong masters don't try to avoid emitting chi energy in the direction of the thyroid gland.)
5. Avoid using frequency E over bones that are fractured. (There is one report of frequency E blocking the healing process in a fractured "splint bone" in a horse. E was stopped, C used, and the bone healed rapidly.)
6. People with seizure disorders. (Pulsed light can trigger seizures in susceptible people but the response is frequency specific. No seizures have been reported following the use of pulsed LEDs in over 20 years.)
7. Avoid shining LED lights directly into the open eye. If you are treating an eye problem keep the lid closed. (We have found that red LED light directly into the open eye is not only safe but can be beneficial. One 80 year-old lady reversed her macular degeneration and is able to read large print and identify faces again.)

Supplements

Oral supplements and liquid minerals have been designed for use in this program and some are available through Chee Energy. Chee Energy never intended to delve into the supplement business but felt a need to do so because of the difficulty finding some of the special nutrients in Rodger's program (the ribose and appropriate doses and forms of minerals for rectal and sublingual use).

Ingredients in the products Rodger recommends are as shown below:

1. *Formula #1* contains the following amounts of elemental minerals per dose (can be given under tongue, rectally, or with juice):

Chromium	1 mcg.
Copper	100 mcg.
Manganese	25 mcg.
Zinc	25 mcg.
Magnesium	25 mg.

These doses should not be exceeded if given rectally because of risk of overdosing. There is no mechanism in the rectum to regulate absorption if an overdose is given.

2. A powder mix containing the following amounts in one level teaspoon:

Vitamin C 2,000 mg.

Niacin   25 mg. (to start, gradually increased in future doses to find the minimal flushing dose)

d-ribose 2,000 mg. (a pentose [five-sided ring compound] used in medical laboratories to stabilize DNA and given orally to increase ATP levels after endurance sports events such as marathons and the Tour de France).

On a daily basis I suggest you take a broad coverage multivitamin/mineral supplement of your choice. You may wish to use other supplements as well and the doses in the above products generally should not create a conflict or overdose. If you are concerned about receiving too much of one of the minerals above you might consider reducing the amount received from another source. Some people may not be able to tolerate niacin and may need to eliminate it.

APPENDIX II: EMBRYOLOGIC ORIGIN OF TISSUES AND NOGIER'S FREQUENCIES

In the 1970s French physician Paul Nogier made what I believe is a monumental discovery that remains largely unrecognized and unappreciated. He found that tissues and organs in the body *resonate* with specific frequencies associated with their early embryologic origins. The pattern is the same in all animals and may be one of the most remarkable in nature. He went on to discover that when tissues and organs became ill he could initiate dramatic healing responses by treating with properly selected resonance frequencies (pulsed on and off).

Early in our development (a few hours after conception) the embryo (then called a blastocyst) consists of a round collection of about 100 identical cells. Indentations appear in the blastocyst that progress toward the center, similar to how one would push two fingers into a balloon until they meet in the middle. The indentations connect and this channel develops into the gastrointestinal tract. Cells begin to specialize along this tube and on the outside of the ball.

Parts of the blastocyst at this stage of formation are called ectoderm (outside skin), endoderm (inside skin) and mesoderm (middle skin). All organs in the body develop from these three tissues. For example, the liver, gall bladder and pancreas grow from the early GI tract. The mesoderm develops into the heart, blood vessels, kidneys, ovaries, spleen, etc. Soon the skin dimples in on one side of the embryo and closes off, forming a tube (the neural tube) that develops into the brain and spinal cord.

Tissues and organs that develop from these three early embryonic tissues are listed below. Embryology is a five-hour course in college and gets quite complex; so don't regard the presentation as complete. For example, many organs are formed from more than one source of tissue. The lining of the bladder comes from endoderm while the bladder muscle forms from mesoderm. Therefore, in treating the bladder a therapist might

155

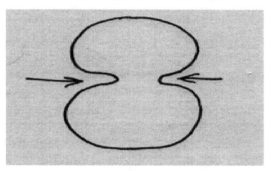

Illustration 1: Dimpling begins from two sides and connects to form a tube that becomes the GI tract.

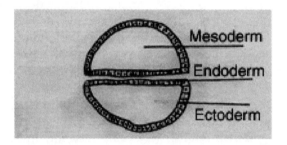

Ilustration 2: The first differentiated cells form on the lining of the tube forming the GI tract and on the outside forming the skin. What's left between will develop into muscles, bones and many internal organs.

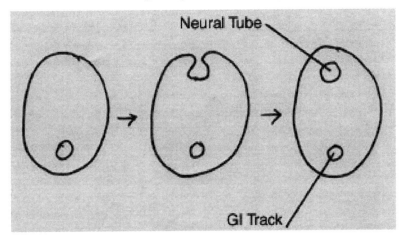

Illustration 3: Cross-section of a developing embryo a little further along. An indentation at the top closes off forming the *neural tube* that develops into the brain and spinal cord.

want to use Nogier's *B* frequency (584 Hz) for the lining tissue and *C* frequency (1,168 Hz) for the muscle. If you wanted to try to stimulate the immune system (thymus plus bone marrow) you might elect to treat over the sternum with the *B* frequency (thymus) plus the *C* frequency (bone marrow).

Tissues From Ectdoderm (Frequency A = 292 Hz)
Central nervous system (brain and spinal cord)
Peripheral nerves
Eye
Ear
Mammary glands
Pituitary gland (anterior and posterior)
Enamel of the teeth
Body of the adrenal gland

Tissues From Endoderm (Frequency B = 584 Hz)
Lining of the GI tract
Lining of the lung
Thyroid gland
Parathyroid gland
Thymus
Liver
Pancreas
Lining of the bladder
Urethra
Auditory tube

Tissues From Mesoderm (Frequency C = 1168 Hz)
Cartilage
Bone
Muscle
Heart
Blood and lymph vessels
Kidney
Ovaries
Testes
Spleen
Cortex of the adrenal

Source for the list of embryologic origins of tissues and organs; Moore KL, Persaud TVN, *The Developing Human: Clinically Oriented Embryology,* WB Saunders Co 1998, New York.

APPENDIX III: MORE SCIENTIFIC REPORTS

A computer search of the National Library of Medicine turned up many additional articles reporting beneficial responses from LLLT. One 1998 review article studied results reported in 1,200 studies with LLLT. Since then, the rate of publication of LLLT articles appears to have accelerated (most of these articles are filed under LLLT and LEPT at www.ncbi.nlm.nih.gov/pubmed).

1.   Nerve function returned faster following an oral surgery procedure with the use of LLLT. *Oral Surg Oral Med Oral Pathol Oral Radiol Endod* 2000 Jan;89(1):12-8.

2.   LLLT reduced postoperative pain on the day of surgery and the day following removal of third molar teeth. *J Can Dent Assoc* 1991 Jul;57(7):584-6

3.   Rats treated with LLLT showed increased immune response when vaccinated with tetanus toxoid (a tetanus shot used to immunize babies). *Indian J Exp Biol* 1999 May;37(5):444-9

4.   LLLT successfully treated a variety of pigmented skin lesions in children. *Semin Cutan Med Surg* 1999 Sep;18(3):233-43

5.   A full thickness skin wound that had not healed for a long period of time in a dog was treated four times in four days with LLLT. The wound healed in 21 days. *Vet Surg* 1999 Jul-Aug;28(4):292-5

6.   LLLT was used to treat 13 people with tumors in their eyes measuring up to 4.5 mm diameter. Tumors disappeared in 8 cases, stabilized in 4 and no response was seen in one. *Klin Oczna* 1999;101(1):23-7. (original in Polish)

7.   Bone fractures in mice healed faster with LLLT. *Lasers Surg Med* 1987;7(1)36-45

8.   Non-pigmented melanoma (skin cancer) cells were treated with a photo sensitizing material then exposed to LLLT pulsed at 10 Hz. A significant decrease in cell survival was observed. *Photochem Photobiol* 1999 Jun;69(6):708-12

9.   204 of the 241 patients (84.7%) treated with maxillofacial region disorders became asymptomatic or improved after treatment with LLLT. The disorders included TMJ pain, trigeminal neuralgia, muscular pain, aphatae, inflammation, and tooth hypersensitivity post-op and small hemangiomas. *J Clin Laser Med Surg* 1998 aug;16(4):223-6

10.   LLLT reduced swelling and other symptoms following mastectomy (removal of the breast). *Lymphology* 1998 Jun;31(2):74-86

11.   LLLT improved wound healing in experimentally induced, full thickness teat wounds in dairy cattle. *Vet Surg* 1997 Mar-Apr;26(2):114-20

12.   LLLT improved wound healing in diabetic mice. The authors conclude that laser biostimulation may be of great benefit in the treatment of chronic wounds that occur as a complication of diabetes mellitus. *Lasers Surg Med* 1997;20(1):56-63

13.   LLLT was shown to activate human immune system cells. *Keio J Med* 1993 Dec;42(4):180-2

14.   LLLT inhibited tumor growth (an implanted glioma, or brain cancer) if applied on the first day after implantation (in mice). *Keio J Med* 1993 Dec;42(4):177-9

15.   Patients being treated with chemotherapy for cancers of the colon, cervix and melanoma were found to have an improvement of natural antitumoral resistance levels and fewer side effects when given adjuvant treatment low energy light therapy. *Klin Khir* 1998;(3):40-1

16.   In patients with eczema (atopic dermatitis) itchy sensation decreased in 71% and skin eruptions in 62%. *Keio J Med* 1993 Dec;42(4):174-6.

17.   Patients with chronic bronchitis were treated by placing a laser diode down the windpipe. The number of phagocytes in the bronchial cells increased 30% and the level of secretory IgA rose 3.5 times, evidence of an immune-stimulating action. *Probl Tuberk* 1991;(6):26-9

18.   LLLT was highly effective in treating unstable angina pains and reduced the risk of heart attacks (myocardial infarction). *Sov Med* 1990;(3):12-5

19.   LLLT produced a moderate reduction in pain and improvement in function in patients with musculoskeletal low back pain. *Arch Phys Med Rehab* 1999 Jun;80(6):647-52 (from the Mayo Clinic)

20.   LLLT was found to restore normal function to immunocompetence cells (strengthens the immune system). *Keio J Med* 1993 Dec;42(4):180-2

21.   LLLT was used to treat "trigger" points (the same as acupuncture points) in patients with muscle pains. Acute pain diminished by 70%, chronic pain by 60%. *J Clin Laser Med Surg* 1996 Aug;14(4):163-7

22.   LLLT increased mitochondrial ATP production, thus vitalizing (increasing) cell energy. *J Clin Laser Med Surg* 1998 Jun;16(3):159-65

23.   LLLT was effective in relieving post-herpetic neuralgia (pain after shingles) in approx. 60% of cases. *Ann Acad Med Singapore* 1993 May;22(3 Suppl)441-2

24.   LLLT improved the appearance of stretch marks of the skin. *Dermatol Surg* 1996 Apr;22(4):332-7

25.   LLLT produced complete healing in recalcitrant ulcers of the skin. *Photodermatol Photoimmunol Photomed* 1999 Feb;15(1):18-21

26.   A double-blind study showed LEPT was an effective modality in the treatment of venous leg ulcers. This study used two cluster probes containing LEDs emitting wavelengths of 660 and 880 nm. *Dermatol Surg* 1998 Dec;24(12):1383-6

27.   Light (non-laser) of different wavelengths slowed mitoses (cell division) in several forms of human cancer cells in tissue culture. Biologic effects were seen at 410 nm, 630 nm, and 805 nm, not at 488 nm, 635 nm, 1,064 nm. and full spectrum white light. *Lasers Surg Med* 1999;25(3):263-71.

28.   LLLT treatment cleared up 92% of recalcitrant viral warts. *Br J Plast Surg* 1999 Oct;52(7):554-8

29.   LLLT increased degranulation of mast cells, one of the possible mechanisms for acceleration of tissue repair in mammals. The highest levels of degranulation were seen with pulsed LLLT at 20 Hz and 292 Hz (Nogier's A frequency). *Lasers Surg Med* 1996;19(4):433-7

30.   Both coherent LLLT and non-coherent (non-laser) red light were found to be clinically effective in treating peptic ulcers. Red, blue and infrared wavelengths all had similar biologic effects in several experiments. This article also pointed out that simple red light has been used in healing for centuries. *Health Physics* 1989;56(5):691-704.

31.   Treatment with infrared LEDs (non-laser) was effective in cases of tendonitis, capsulitis and myofascial pain. *J Neurol Orthop Med Surg* 1996:16:242-245

32.   Another report on LLLT from Israel reiterated that coherent light is not required to achieve beneficial results and non-coherent narrow-band appropriate light therapy is sufficient to produce most or all of them. *Health Physics* 1989;56(5):687-90.

33.   An unpublished abstract of a study on mouse cancer cells in tissue culture by Priscilla F. Strang PhD of the Department of Pharmacology, University of Miami School of Medicine, Miami, FL USA and presented at the 6th Congress of the International Society for Laser Surgery and Medicine, Jerusalem, Israel, October 13-18, 1985.

   THE EFFECTS OF LACER ™ LIGHT ON NEOPLASTIC CELLS

   Although high intensity laser is thought to be carcinogenic (cancer causing) low power lasers have been quite useful in such areas as wound healing, in the growth of healthy tissue and reduced scar formation. The LACER ™ stimulator from CEFCO Inc (the trademarked name for a device containing several infrared LEDs) gives the operator the ability to select the frequency of pulses (on and off) discovered by Paul Nogier MD of France. A cultured mouse myeloma cell was chosen for the study. The study tested the effect of duration of treatment on myeloma cell survival compared to untreated myeloma cells. Frequencies and times of treatment are shown. Treatment was repeated daily for seven days.

TABLE: Growth Rates of Treated Cancer Cells (Untreated controls=100%)

Frequency	F	G	A	B	C	D	E
5 minutes	100%	100%	100%	-	55%	75%	23%
10 minutes	100%	100%	44%	-	31%	88%	19%
20 minutes	100%	64%	55%	77%	55%	55%	42%

All of the cancer cells continued to grow in the tissue cultures. The figures show the growth rate of myeloma cells treated with pulsed LEDs compared to the growth rate of untreated myeloma cells, which would be 100%.

Several findings are of interest. Only some of the frequencies were effective in reducing the rate of cell growth and the optimal exposure was 10 minutes on frequency E.

Another observation was the formation of gas bubbles with the A and B frequencies. The bubbles appeared after 5 minutes of treatment and continued to be produced for several hours after termination of the treatments (presumed to be hydrogen gas). Gas formation was seen only with these frequencies. In addition the cultures became more acidic (pH dropped) with all of the frequencies but this did not occur until after 10 or 20 minutes of treatment.

34. A panel of high intensity blue LEDs was <u>more effective</u> than conventional phototherapy (ultraviolet) in treatment of jaundice of the newborn in a double-blind study This clears the way for the development of portable units for home use that don't pose a risk of eye damage. *Pediatr Res* 1998 Nov;44(5):804-9. (from Stanford University)

35. High intensity blue LEDs were as effective as conventional phototherapy in treating jaundice of the newborn. *J Pediatr* 2000 June;136(6):771-4. (from Isreal))

Summary

As discussed previously, researchers reporting studies with LLLT are using true lasers with the power turned down to non-injurious levels similar to those delivered by LED devices. The fact that LED devices can produce the same beneficial effects has been confirmed in veterinary practices for the past 18 years, in humans, and in a growing number of scientific studies.

The same observation is being reported in the scientific literature. Russian Tiina Kura, author of the article listed as # 30 above, states that, "Laser biostimulation is a photobiological phenomenon. Coherent (laser) light is not needed." Her article contains several examples of biologic effects from non-laser sources of light. The authors of reference #32 make this same point.

LEDs were the source of light therapy in published studies identified as references 26, 27, 31, 34 and 35 above. They were used as well in the unpublished studies listed as #33 above and the rabbit tendon healing study mentioned in Chapter 2 (page 24).

In most studies the light energy was applied continuously. I found only two published studies in which a low level laser energy was pulsed at frequencies described by Nogier (the rat study described in Chapter 2 by McKibbon where nerves to the skin were cut and grew back in treated areas but not in untreated areas, and reference #29 above).

Few people know of Nogier's discoveries today. They come from an obscure source in acupuncture and most researchers in the area of LLLT either lack knowledge of the principles of Chinese Medicine or may prefer to avoid mention of any such connection to their work to avoid controversy.

From our own experiences and those of others, we believe the following is an accurate assessment of the level of knowledge in this field at the present time.

164

1. Wavelength (color) of the light source makes a difference. Most beneficial biologic effects of light therapy have been seen with wavelengths in the blue, red, and infrared ranges.
2. Biologic effects and speed of healing are magnified when effective wavelengths of light are pulsed on and off at optimal pulsation rates discovered by Paul Nogier MD of France.
3. Choice of frequencies may determine if a study (or treatment) is going to be successful or not. For example, nerve tissue ideally should be treated with frequency A (292 Hz), not with a randomly selected frequency or instrument determined 10 Hz or 1000 Hz. The immune system (thymus and bone marrow) should be treated with frequency C (for mesoderm), not some other arbitrarily selected frequency
4. Stimulation of the energy system works best with doses that are adequate but not too high. Increasing power levels may negate potentially positive benefits and with the use of LLLT tissue damage could occur.
5. We find that treatments with LEDs are more effective when used in combination with supplements of trace minerals, use of the anal heater, the infrared sauna, and a pattern of good health habits.
6. All of this information will need to be modified in the future as we learn more about new designs of red, white, and blue LEDs that are combined with geometric patterns and off-on frequencies. These new instruments give off energy that can be felt passing through lead that does not diminish with distance. These are characteristics of chi itself. Therefore these new instruments have the capacity to normalize cell functions (heal) through the delivery of light in the usual sense (delivery of Joules) as well as through the delivery of an additional energy that defies explanation and violates the laws of physics.

165

In a new approach to cancer a photosensitizing drug from a plant source is injected into a vein. Two days later the compound is cleared from the body except for the skin and tumors. The tumor then is treated with the direct application of red light (660 nm) either from a low level laser **or** LED device. This treatment has been used with some success in several cancers.

After about 15 years of research the method gained FDA approval for use in cancers of the lung and esophagus. The approach is limited to tumors that can be reached with a light directly as the source of the light must touch the tumor tissue directly. An internet search for the word Photofrin in January 2003 brought up 2,215 sites. A search for "photodynamic therapy" produced 19,302 sites. Many other similar products are under investigation.

APPENDIX IV: RESOURCES

Facilities offering elements of the program:

1. Alaska Pain Reduction Center, 3275 Montclaire Ct, Anchorage AK 99503. Phone 907/274-0042, Fax 907/274-0572. Web: www.alaskaelectrolytes.com. This is the program operated by Laura Lamoreux as described in Chapter 4 under Case Reports.

Resources for equipment:

(Prices subject to change.)
1. Chee Energy, PO Box 5009, Coeur d'Alene, ID 83814. W 2385 Bolivar Ave, Coeur d'Alene ID, 83815. Orders only: 888-263-9214. Customer Service: 800 442 8029. Fax 208-664 3452. Web ordering and information at www..cheeenergy.com. Source of instruments and supplements used in Rodger's program. Swiss made anal heater device at $379. *X-Light* hand held LED device with color and pulsing options at $345. *Energy-Balancer* 13 by 9 inch pad with 63 red, white, blue, and infrared LEDs with 7 frequency options and 3 color options $595. *Red-Carpet* 16-inch pad of pulsed red and infrared LEDs (96 diodes) with controller at $525. Light device for inflammatory skin sores $199. One-person portable infrared sauna $695.

2. Light Energy Company, 1056 NW 179th Place, Seattle, WA 98177. Tel: 1 800-544-4826. Sells LED devices with red LEDs, pulsed or continuous, (not Nogier's frequencies). Sells a variety of full spectrum lights developed by John Ott.

3. Diomedics, at www.diomedics.com. Source of non-pulsed LED cluster probes in multiple colors (up to 8) with prices ranging from $129 to the $2,000 range.

4. Anodyne Therapy Systems at 4343 S. Buckley Rd, Suite 310, Aurora, CO 80015. Tel 303-699-8700. e-mail at: rmht@rockymountainhealth.com. Source of 4 ¼ " x 2 ¼ " pads each containing 60 non-pulsed infrared LEDs. Unit of 4 pads with controller priced at $4,695.
5. Cefco, Inc. PO Box 429, Inola, OK 74036. Tel: 918 543 8415. Fax: 918 543 2554. Company run by Dan Parris, pioneer in the design and manufacture of pulsed infrared and red LED pads and other LED devices for veterinarians and animal use since 1982. One long-standing product is a 60 infrared diode cluster probe (pulsed at Nogier's frequencies) for $1,250 that is a popular item with veterinarians.
6. BioScan, Inc. 6 Walden Rd., Corrales, NM 87048, Tel: 800-388-2712. Manufactures and sells equipment similar to Cefco to horse and other animal owners directly.
7. Light Energy Company, 1056 NW 179th Place, Seattle, WA 98177. Tel: 1 800-544-4826. Sells a device with a single red LED pulsed or continuous, and a device with three red LEDs pulsed at 5 frequencies (not Nogier's frequencies). Sells full spectrum lights developed by John Ott.

Resources for Acupuncture Materials and Books

1. M.E.D. Servi-Systems, 8 Sweetnam Dr., Stittsville, Ontario, Canada K2S 1G2. 800-267 6868 (North America). Web site: www.medserv.ca
2. Redwing Book Co, 44 Linden Street, Brookline, MA 02445 USA. Phone 1-800-873-3946 USA, 1-888-873-3947 Canada. Web: www.redwingbooks.com

Informational resources

1. The Qigong Institute, 561 Berkeley, Menlo Park, CA 94025. Phone: 650-323-1221. Net address:

www.qigonginstitute, org. Offers scientific information on qigong including a data-base on CD.

2. Courses in auriculotherapy and auricular medicine (of Dr. Nogier) by Mikhael Adams. Contact MED Servi-Systems listed above.

3. *The Townsend Letter for Doctors and Patients,* a journal (10 issues per year) covering the large field of complementary and alternative medicine including articles on energy medicine. Tel: 360 385 6021. Fax: 360 385 0699.

APPENDIX V: CHINESE QIGONG

I previously described how my interest in Chinese qigong began and progressed to co-authoring a book on the subject (Chapter 1). This led to the discovery that Rodger had the abilities of a *qigong master* without going through the usual ordeal of practicing four hours every day for a lifetime.

It means little for someone to self-declare as a qigong master. A true qigong master is a person who has a proven and documented ability to heal others by emitting energy (qi, pronounced chee) from the body. Some people are born with this ability, such as Chang Bao Shung who treated Premier Deng Xiao Ping of China for one hour per day for many years. Deng lived on and on with advanced prostate cancer and just wouldn't die. His body had been riddled with cancer for many years when he finally passed away in his 90s.

Chang Bao Shung was so valuable an asset he either traveled with Deng under bodyguards or lived in luxury as a virtual prisoner in the downtown Beijing headquarters of the Communist Party adjacent to the Imperial Palace. In 1990 Dr. Kong tried to arrange for us to meet Chang by attempting to sneak him out of the compound at three in the morning. The effort was unsuccessful because he was too heavily guarded.

After the Cultural Revolution came to an end in 1976 qigong practice, which had been repressed for ten years, came out into the open. The Chinese government was forced to act on the matter because tales of spectacular cures following treatment by qigong masters were spreading. Qigong in some ways resembles a religious superstition and many political leaders wanted it banned for good. They called upon academics to delve into the subject using the highest standards of science. Qigong passed the test of scientific scrutiny and with no other option available to them government officials allowed it to become a treatment modality in Traditional Chinese Medicine hospitals (funded and operated by the government). More research followed over the next 20 years.

Forever pragmatic the government of China also realized there was no way it could provide expensive western style medicine to its 1.2 billion people so it began to encourage the use of qigong. The United States can't even afford its own medical system as currently practiced. China will be better served if its health care system uses more of the proven effective and less expensive old ways (and alternative approaches from the west) with the use of fewer drugs and surgeries.

More recently, the school of Falun Gong appeared on the scene and attracted over 80 million followers in less than a decade. The size of the movement triggered a paranoid reaction among governmental leaders who feared its potential to turn into a political movement. As a result, many qigong masters went into hiding or were arrested and support for research in qigong is on the decline (as of 2,000).

According to Ken Sancier PhD of the Qigong Institute (see Resources), there are now 1,660 citations to scientific studies in qigong, many coming from the finest academic institutions in China. A few of the more dramatic findings are as follows:

1. Qigong masters demonstrated that higher percentages of bacteria could be killed the longer they held a test tube containing a bacteria solution simply by pumping energy into it.

2. The heart rate of rats was increased or slowed according to the mental intent of the qigong master.

3. In 45 people with long-term paralysis of limbs, 93% regained movement to various degrees and only7% did not improve at all. In other words, the chance of observing some sort of miracle in the study was 93%.

4. Some outright cures of the most lethal forms of cancer (lung, pancreas, ovary, stomach) have been reported where no other treatment was involved to muddy the water.

5. Emitted qi killed human stomach cancer cells in tissue cultures at the China Immunology Research Center in

Beijing. In one study 25% of stomach cancer cells died and that study was repeated 41 times with the same results.

Photo 1: Human stomach cancer cells from a tissue culture magnified 3,200 times by electron microscopy. Note the rough surfaces of cells.

6. Qigong practice was highly effective in treatment of high blood pressure. 85% of 639 patients were able to control their high blood pressure without drugs.
7. In a barbaric sounding but highly interesting study small test pigs were given spinal cord injuries by stretching the spine (not severing it). All 6 pigs treated with qigong

regained the ability to walk, none of the 6 untreated pigs did so.

8. Many studies have shown qigong practice can improve function of the immune system.

Across China researchers studied high level qigong masters to determine what physical energies might be emitted from their bodies. Along with my co-author of the qigong book,

Photo 2: A human stomach cancer cell after treatment for one hour with emitted qi. The surface is smooth with pores (holes) indicating impending death. Photos courtesy of Feng Li-da MD PhD and Qian Ju Qing of the China Immunology Research Center in Beijing.

Effie Poy Yew Chow PhD, and Ken Sancier PhD, president of the Qigong Institute, I had the opportunity to visit several qigong research facilities in China in 1990. Energies reported to be emitted at abnormally high levels included infrared, infrasound, raman spectra, electromagnetic, microwave, ultraviolet spectra, magnetic field generation and electrostatic field generation.

Qigong masters were examined in the resting state and in the so-called *qigong state* (pumped up and ready to heal). Energies emitted from the laogong energy point in the palm increased 100 to 1,000 times over the resting state. Different qigong masters were found to emit different energies. Some emitted one form of energy, some multiple energies, and some, with outstanding healing records, none of these energies. This demonstrates the elusiveness of the energy of qigong and how much more there is to learn about this phenomenon.

I like to point out that though people may say they know nothing about qigong they very likely have a practitioner of simple qigong principles living in their home. I am referring to the family dog or cat. As mentioned above the basic elements of qigong practice are clearing the mind, stretching and breathing with the abdomen. I am certain you would agree your dog or cat has no problem keeping its mind clear, especially your dog. They also breathe with the diaphragm (you can check this while your pet sleeps) and perform stretching exercises upon arising. Enough said.

Many methods of qigong practice are patterned after animals and birds. One very agile method mimics the movements of a monkey (on speed). We once saw a method in which the qigong master's body movements copied the writhing of a snake. This fellow did his routine in the vertical position, not slithering on the floor, and he must be one of the most flexible men in the world.

Human babies breathe with the abdomen (diaphragm) and professional singers must learn this method of breathing if they are to have long successful careers. These practices are similar to qigong and for unknown reasons this good health habit is trained out of us when we are young.

The Yan Xin Physics Studies

In 1990 the most famous qigong master in China was Dr. Yan Xin (pronounced Yen Sheen). Yan Xin learned qigong from his grandfather and practiced four hours a day from the age of four. He later earned a doctor of TCM degree from the University of Traditional Chinese Medicine in Chongqing (Chungking) in the early 1980s. His healing record helped qigong to become accepted by the masses in China in the mid 1980s.

One miraculous case was that of Yang Jixang, a 36 year-old man who was injured at work in a fall. Yang suffered a skull fracture, subdural hematoma (bleeding between the skull and brain) and a compression fracture of L-2 with a spinal cord injury. Emergency surgery removed the blood clot on his brain and eight days later his spine was fused at the fracture site. After the injury Yang remained permanently paralyzed from the waist down.

Yan Xin first saw Yang seven months after his injury (after normal healing and movement has been seen to occur). He went to a Buddhist temple ten kilometers away and proceeded to treat Yang all night from that distance. During the treatment Yang flushed, broke out in sweats and was unable to sleep. After the treatment he slept for nine hours, got up out of bed, and walked around his home on crutches. Five months later, on October 7, 1987, with only a slight limp, Yang, qigong master Yan, and eleven other miraculously cured people walked up the Great Wall on a live broadcast of a popular national television news program similar to our *60 Minutes.*

Almost overnight Yan Xin became a national hero and in great demand. Qigong associations flew him all over the country lecturing to sold-out crowds in sports arenas. While speaking some people experienced involuntary movements and many later reported recoveries from illnesses. *China Central Television*

176

broadcast a documentary about him with the title *Chinese Superman: Yan Xin* and his fame spread further.

Yan was not shy about boasting of his powers and said he could manipulate matter with his energies. This rubbed the scientific community the wrong way and professor Lu Zuyin of the Institute for High Energy Physics of the Chinese Academy of Sciences was asked to perform tests on Yan. Lu was a nuclear physicist and highly regarded as one of China's top scientists (Lu is now deceased).

Lu spoke perfect English as he told us the story of his work with Yan Xin. In the beginning Lu was a total skeptic. In cooperation with other scientists he set up eight experiments designed to destroy Yan Xin and expose him as a fraud. These experiments are summarized in *Miracle Healing From China...Qigong* and abstracts are available from the Qigong Institute (see Appendix VII, Resources---Eight Scientific Articles translated from *Yeng Xing's Scientific Qigong* published by China Books, 1988). I would like to describe what to me is the most remarkable of the studies.

Yan Xin claimed he could increase the decay rate of a radioactive compound. Nuclear physicists say decay rates are very constant. Lu set up a study in his laboratory to test Yan Xin and he showed us the instruments used in the study.

From ten feet away Yan Xin emitted his qi in the direction of a slug of the radioactive compound Americium-241 about the size of a nickel. The slug was placed in a slot halfway between two instruments that record radioactivity levels digitally. Two instruments were used to guard against false readings that might occur if any of the equipment was bumped accidentally.

Lu told us he was shocked to the core with the first test. The decay rate went up 1.05% and that **violates the laws of physics**. Control slugs were stable with normal fluctuations of less than 0.06%. In more than 40 repetitions Yan Xin altered the decay rate up or down to a similar degree according to his mental intent. Daily readings were taken on treated slugs after the tests, and the decay rate slowly returned to normal, but it took eleven days to do so.

Lu was to be shocked further when Yan Xin achieved the same effect from great distances. On one scheduled test day Yan was in Canton, 1,250 miles to the south. Yan called Lu and told him to set up the equipment and at an appointed time he would alter the slug from where he was. Lu thought this was ridiculous but set up the equipment anyway. Results were the same as when Yan was in Beijing. Yan later repeated the test from Chonqing with the same results and then told Lu he could do the same from anywhere in the world. Lu had no idea what kind of phenomenon he had stumbled into but after completing all eight studies on Yan Xin he became a believer in qigong.

Dr. Kong brought both professor Lu and Yan Xin to San Francisco in 1990 to participate in a conference on qigong and I had the opportunity to sit next to Yan Xin at lunch. Dr. Yan is a soft-spoken man, a Buddhist and total vegan. During the meal he asked that a clean knife be brought to the table to cut something in his vegetarian soup because the only knife on the table had touched butter. Evidently he believed some bad vibes would come his way if he used a knife that even touched food from an animal. (Photo in color photo section)

Guo Lin Qigong and Cancer

Guo Lin developed cancer of the uterus in the 1960s. The cancer returned in her bladder and most of that organ was removed surgically. The cancer returned again and she was declared to be untreatable with only six months to live.

She decided to treat herself with a style of qigong she learned from her grandfather. She was innovative and experimented with body motions she sensed were good for her own energy balance. She developed a graceful walking form of qigong and practiced it diligently. The cancer gradually went away and she died of other causes years later in 1984.

On our tour of qigong facilities in 1990 we visited a park in Beijing where people with advanced cancer gather every Sunday to learn and practice this form of qigong. We observed groups of people winding through trees in the park in serpentine files in unison. The smoothness of their movements was impressive.

First we were introduced to Guo Lin's husband. Then we met many people who told us their personal experiences of how they recovered completely from advanced cancers of the liver, pancreas, lung, stomach and other organs. After this a western trained medical doctor who was very fluent in English and was treating her own cancer with Quo Lin Qigong took us to a warm hotel lobby and demonstrated all the variations of the method.

In the main version of Guo Lin Qigong the feet meet the ground very deliberately heel first and the hands pass back and forth in a horizontal plane just below the navel. Timed with walking movements are vocal sounds that sound like "Chee-chee-hoo, chee-chee-hoo."

Only people who have survived serious cancers themselves through the use of Guo Lin Qigong are considered qualified to be instructors in the method. We were told over 1,000,000 people in China were treating themselves with Guo Lin Qigong in 1990.

Photo 3: Guo Lin, Courtesy of the Guo Lin Research Society, Beijing

APPENDIX VI: The Scientific Validation of Quantum Medicine

The following article was written by Paul Yanick. Jr., PhD, president of the American Academy of Quantum Medicine, appeared in the *Townsend Newsletter for Physicians and Patients* in July of 2000 and is reproduced with his permission:

Quantum medicine provides an energy-based medical paradigm that combines a wide spectrum of multidisciplinary health assessment protocols in an attempt to address the full complexities of chronic illness. Quantum medical practitioners view disease as a disruption, cessation, or distortion of the body's energetic anatomy along caused by a wide range of stress factors (nutrient deficiencies, toxicity, infections, etc.). Instead of suppressing the symptoms of this disharmony (pain, inflammation, etc.), these practitioners approach illness with the intent of eliminating the disharmony with bursts of energy or a specific resonance stimulations that correct the disharmony, eliminate stress or causative factors, and enhancing innate healing.

In the 1920s and 1930s Dr. Harold Saxon Burr of *Yale University* researched the energetic qualities of different forms of life. For example, Burr observed changes in the electrical field of trees to seasonal changes, sunlight and darkness, cycles of the moon, and sunspots. In humans, he noted that emotional stress affected the body's energy field (*Transactions of the American Neurology Association* 63, 1939). When observing hormonal changes in women, he was able to record a voltage change just before ovulation and a subsequent drop in voltage just as the egg is released (*American Journal of Obstetrics and Gynecology* 44, 1942). The most fascinating of his discoveries pertains to the voltage changes that would allow Burr and his colleagues to define malignant tissue and predict when a woman would develop cancer of the cervix (*Science*, 105, 1947). An excellent review of his forty-three years of research is summarized in his book *Blueprint for*

Immortality: The Electric Patterns of Life. This breakthrough book reveals important scientific discoveries:

1. All living things—from men to mice, from trees to seeds—are formed and controlled by electrodynamic fields that Burr defined as *L fields* (*Yale Journal of Biological Medicine*, 16, 1944; *Science*, 103, 1946; *Proceedings of National Academy of Science*, 32, 1946).
2. L fields are the basic blueprints of all life (*Yale Journal of Biological Medicine*, 17, 1945; *Federal Proceedings*, 6, 1947; *Medical Physiology*, 1950).
3. L fields are informational and can reveal physical and mental conditions in order for doctors to diagnose illness before the usual symptoms develop (*Yale Journal of Biological Medicine*, 14, 1942; *Yale Journal of Biological Medicine*, 19, 1947; *Yale Journal of Biological Medicine*, 21, 1949).

Carlo Rubbia, a 1984 Nobel Laureate, made an astounding observation on the magnitude of biological information fields which he **reports is far greater than biochemical or biomolecular information in the human body**. Consequently, any medical field that examines only the physical body is only assessing a small and inconsequential part of human anatomy.

An American neurologist, Albert Abrams, M.D. who taught pathology at *Stanford University's* medical school in California, made the following scientific observations (*New Concepts in Diagnosis and Treatment*, San Francisco, Philopolis Press, 1916):

1. Unknown resonances or waves were omitted from pathological tissue that can be used with great accuracy to locate an infection or pathology, and
2. Resonant frequencies or radiations from quinine eliminated the unknown resonances associated with malaria and mercurial salts stopped syphilis radiations (the same was true of other known antidotes).

In a series of 25 clinical trials, Dr. William Boyd confirmed Abrams research and with 100 percent accuracy was able to identify chemicals and tissues without visual or any other clues except their resonances. In 1924, the Royal Society of Medicine investigated Boyd's claims and found them valid (*Royal Society of Medicine*, 1925). The committee was impressed with the new diagnostic capabilities of Boyd's methods.

Nobel Prize double-nominee, Robert O. Becker, M.D. reported that the electromagnetic resonance behaves in the human body in a similar fashion to magnetic-resonance imaging (MRI) and that the body's innate resonances could be used to heal and explain problematic health issues (*Cross Currents: The Perils of Electropollution, The Promise of Electromedicine*, Tarcher/Putman, 1990).

A controlled, research study on rats by the US Naval Research Center, Bethesda, Maryland (*Biomagnetics*, 7, 1986) documented that the magnetic resonance from lithium (not an oral dose) was able to subdue behavior and depress the central nervous system. This study is important because it documents significant biological effects from minute radiations similar to homeopathic medicines.

Another brilliant researcher, George Lakhovsky, published *The Secret of Life* in 1925 revealing that "every living cell is essentially dependent on its nucleus which is the center of oscillations and gives off radiations." His research has important health implications. Lakhovsky's book defines life and disease as a battle between healthy resonances and the unhealthy resonances of cells against microbes and other toxins. When we consider that the sun is the center of our solar system, and life could not exist without it giving off radiations that set up oscillations in living matter, it becomes obvious that energy principles work on the same universal laws, be they atoms, cells, or solar systems.

Famous US surgeon and founder of the Cleveland Clinic in Ohio, George Crile, M.D. supported Lakhovsky's finding with independent studies that were reported in his book *The Phenomena of Life: A Radio-electric Interpretation*, which was printed in 1936. He states, "electricity is the energy that drives the organism." He likened the cell to a battery and stated "It is clear that in the second half of life the electrical potential of the elderly patient as a whole or of this or that organ, has been very much reduced and that by so much, the margin of safety has been dangerously diminished." In the 1937 *British Medical Journal*, Sir Thomas Lewis defined an independent cutaneous nerve system of pathways that was not composed of nerve fibers.

Using electromyography (EMG), Dr. Valerie Hunt at UCLA discovered that the body emits oscillations between the "noise" of normal muscle contractions. With sophisticated equipment, Hunt was able to monitor fluctuations in the body's electromagnetic energy levels (*Progress Report: A Study of Structural Integration from Neuromuscular Energy Field and Emotional Approaches*, UCLA, 1977).

Further documentation of the body's electromagnetic energies came from photographic techniques discovered by Semyon Kirlian in Russia. With the interaction of a high-frequency electric discharge and a photographic plate he captured the energetic imprints of living organisms on the film. Further research by scientists at the Kirov State University of Kazakhstan and by M.K. Gaikin, M.D. correlated these measurements with traditional Chinese medicine concepts of energy flow. I found some of the most impressive work with Kirilian photography in Peter Mandel's book *Energy Emission Analysis*. Mandel work was important for the following reasons:

1. His findings were based on over 800,000 photographs (energy emission analysis or EEA), which documented the beginning and end points of classical acupuncture.
2. All irregularities of bodily functions were depicted on the photographs
3. He based his therapeutic intervention on either the positive or negative EEA macrographs.

Validation and Anatomical Documentation of Meridian Pathways

While some researchers have documented the electromagnetic resonances of life, other have documented what

184

ancient Chinese medical wisdom has taught for thousands of years. The following are highlights of some of the research that validates the existence of the acupoints and meridian pathways:

- During the 1960s Professor Kim Bong Han studied the acupoints of animals. He injected radioactive P^{32} (an isotope of phosphorus) into an acupoint and followed the uptake of the substance into surrounding tissue. With microautoradiography techniques, he discovered that the P^{32} followed the path of the classical acupuncture meridians (*The Acupuncturist*, 1, 1967).

- In 1985, Pierre de Vernejoul at the University of Paris injected radioactive markers in acupuncture points. Using a gamma-camera imaging, he tracked the movement of the isotope. His findings indicated that the tracer followed the pathways of the classical meridian lines at the speed of 30 cm in 4-6 minutes. As a control, he also made random injections in the skin, vessels, and lymphatic channels documenting that there was no migration at these sites. (*The Kirilian Aura*, Doubleday, 1974; *Bulletin of the Academy of National Medicine* 169, 1985).

- Using electronographic body scans, researchers documented meridian pathways (*Electrographic Imaging in Medicine and Biology* Neville Spearman Ltd.,1983).

- In studies similar to Dr. Burr, Professor Kim found that the meridian ducts were formed within fifteen hours of conception in the embryonic chick before the rudimentary organs were formed (*Design for Destiny* Ballentine Books, 1974).

- In another experiment, Professor Kim severed the liver meridian in a frog and observed the subsequent changes in the liver tissue. Shortly after severing the meridian, he discovered enlarged liver cells. Three days later he noted serious vascular degeneration throughout the entire liver.

- Dr. William Tiller of *Stanford University* observed close to a twenty-fold drop in electrical resistance at the acupoints (*Energy Field Observations*, 1988).

185

- Dr. Hiroshi Motoyama AMI Machine (short for Apparatus for Measuring the Functions of the Meridians and Corresponding Internal Organ) research on over five thousand patients documented strong correlations between weaker meridians and underlying disease states in associated organ systems (*Science and the Evolution of Consciousness*, Autumn Press, 1978).

- Reinhold Voll, M.D., who discovered electroacupuncture techniques, spent two decades studying acupuncture points and their related meridians. Voll's discovery that almost all Chinese acupuncture points could be detected by a change in skin resistance was of incredible importance to the birth of Quantum Medicine (*American Acupuncture* 8, 1980).

All the above studies support the teachings of Chinese medicine. In brief, doctors of Chinese medicine believe that illness is caused by energetic imbalances. Certainly Kim's research supports the concept that meridian changes *precede* physical organ dysfunction. Thus the integrity and balance of the acupuncture meridian system is crucial to detecting illness in the earliest possible stages before organ degeneration take place. Yet it is important to note that traditional Chinese theories were developed thousands of years ago when the planet was not as polluted and food was not genetically-engineered, toxic or depleted in nutrients. Hence, we may not be able to rely solely on old Chinese remedies and theories now and in the 21st century. Over the past decade, my research with the *Yanick Quantum Energy Method*® on thousands of natural products that were tested against stressed organs, glands and systems of the body, revealed that over ninety percent of supplements currently available were toxic or had poor energetic and biochemical bioactivity. This research was confirmed by *In Vitro* screening studies of 196 natural products that found 191 toxic or ineffective with only 5 or 2.5 percent non-toxic (*Journal of the American Nutraceutical Association*, Vol 2:1, 25-41, Winter, 1996). For the best clinical results, quantum medical practitioners use non-toxic, clinically effective supplements that contain the correct resonances of healthy organs, glands and systems of the body and the correct nourishment to support and strengthen weak physiology. This powerful synergism in supplement choices allows the body to discharge toxins, eliminate opportunistic infections, and correct nutritional deficiency states in the shortest time possible.

Assessing the Stress-related Origins of Disease

Most standard medical textbooks attribute 50 to 80 percent of all disease to stress-related origins. Emerging from Quantum Medicine and its attendant philosophy is the view that a wide spectrum of stressors can be assessed by observing subtle energy systems that govern physiology and give rise to chronic disease. Causative agents that are not always detectable at the biochemical level, commonly manifest an attendant perturbation at the energetic level. Foundational research that supports the basis of Quantum Medicine has provided a clear mandate for the necessity of considering the variables of energetic anatomy in attempting to comprehend complex, mulitsystem disease. It is evident that the energetic context of health disorders, needs to be considered with the traditional biochemical model and that neither can stand alone. For example, using the meridian system as a way to determine biochemical stressors and organ responses to stress factors can synchronize enzymes and create an amplified crystalline resonant field that propels nutrients deep within the cells of the body (*Townsend Letter for Doctors*, April, 2000), thereby improving nutrient uptake. As an added bonus, matching the correct resonant frequencies to meridian representations of organs and systems of the body enhances electron transfer functions and stabilizes molecular defenses, thereby reducing oxidative stress.

187

BIBLIOGRAPHY

Allanch, J *Color Me Healing*, Element Books LTD 1997 Shaftesbury Dorset, England.

Becker R, Seldon G, *The Body Electric*, 1985 Quill NY.

Complementary and Alternative Veterinary Medicine, editors Wynn SG, Schoen AM, 1998 Mosby, St. Louis.

Eisenberg D, *Encounters With Qi*, 1985 WW Norton and Co.

Gerber R, *Vibrational Medicine*, 1988 Bear and Co, Santa Fe, New Mexico.

Kaptchuk TJ, *The Web That Has No Weaver*, 1983 Congdon and Weed, Inc, NY.

Lewis LG, Treatment of Prostatitis by local heat: the Elliot Treatment Regulator, *J Urol* 1936:681-6.

Li Hongzhi, *China Falun Gong*, 1998 Falun Fo Fa Pub Co, Hong Kong.

Lieberman J, *Light: Medicine of the Future*, 1991 Bear and Co Santa Fe New Mexico.

Light Years Ahead, editor Brian Breiling, 1996 Light Years Ahead Pub, Tiburon CA.

Maciocia G, *Tongue Diagnosis in Chinese Medicine*, 1987 Eastland Press, Seattle.

BIBLIOGRAPHY

Allanch, J *Color Me Healing*, Element Books LTD 1997 Shaftesbury Dorset, England.

Becker R, Seldon G, *The Body Electric*, 1985 Quill NY.

Complementary and Alternative Veterinary Medicine, editors Wynn SG, Schoen AM, 1998 Mosby, St. Louis.

Eisenberg D, *Encounters With Qi*, 1985 WW Norton and Co.

Gerber R, *Vibrational Medicine*, 1988 Bear and Co, Santa Fe, New Mexico.

Kaptchuk TJ, *The Web That Has No Weaver*, 1983 Congdon and Weed, Inc, NY.

Lewis LG, Treatment of Prostatitis by local heat: the Elliot Treatment Regulator, *J Urol* 1936:681-6.

Li Hongzhi, *China Falun Gong*, 1998 Falun Fo Fa Pub Co, Hong Kong.

Lieberman J, *Light: Medicine of the Future*, 1991 Bear and Co Santa Fe New Mexico.

Light Years Ahead, editor Brian Breiling, 1996 Light Years Ahead Pub, Tiburon CA.

Pontinen PJ, *Low Level Laser Therapy,* 1992 Art Urpo, Tempere (Finland).

Maciocia G, *Tongue Diagnosis in Chinese Medicine*, 1987 Eastland Press, Seattle.

McGee CT, Chow EPY, *Miracle Healing From China...Qigong*, 1994 Medipress, Coeur d'Alene ID.

Nogier PMF, *Handbook to Auriculotherapy*, 1981 Maisonneuve, France.

Ohishiro T, Calderhead RG, *Low Level Laser Therapy: A Practical Introduction*, 1988 John Wiley and Sons Ltd.

Ott J, *Health and Light*, 1973 Devin-Adair, Old Greenwich CT.

Pontinen, Pekka J., *Low Level Laser Therapy as a Medical Treatment Modality*, Art Urpo Ltd, Tampere (Finland) 1992.

Schauss AG, *Minerals, Trace Elements and Health*, 1995 Biosocial Publications, Tacoma WA.

Schroeder HR, *The Trace Elements and Man*, 1973 Devin-Adair, Old Greenwich CT.

Smith CW, Best S, *Electromagnetic Man*, 1989 St. Martin's Press, NY.

Yanick, Paul Jr., *Quantum Medicine*, 2000. Available through the American Academy of Quantum Medicine, 652 Route 299, Suite 101, Highland, New York 12528, USA, for $50.00.

Yeng Xing's (Yan Xin) Scientific Qigong, 1988 China Books Press. English abstracts available from the Qigong Institute, 561 Berkeley, Menlo Park CA 94025. Phone 650 323 1221, Web address www.qigonginstitute.org

Wu Wei-Ping, *Chinese Acupuncture*, 1962 Health Science Press, Northamptonshire England.

INDEX

Healing Energies of Heat and Light

194

COLOR PICTURE SECTION

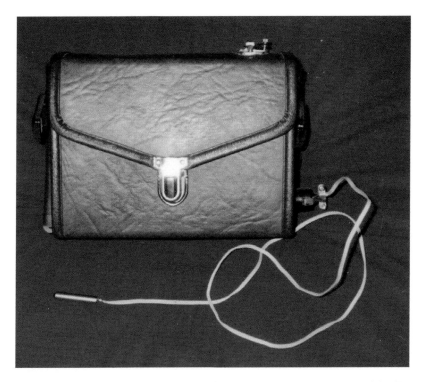

Chapter 1-1. Prototype of the Thermotherapy instrument built in 1978. The tiny probe on the end of the wire had a heating element but the unit had no thermostat. The user was forced to turn the device on and off repeatedly to prevent overheating.

Chapter 1-2. Rodger's anal heater thermotherapy device equipped with a thermostat. After two clinical studies showed dramatic responses in treating hemorrhoids the FDA cleared the device in 1982 and it was sold for 20 years until the supply was exhausted. The dial allowed the user to select a comfortable probe temperature up to a maximum level of 113° F (set by the FDA with a safety margin to prevent burns).

Chapter 1-3. Rodger's hand in what is referred to as the *qigong state*, ready to emit his chi. When he does qigong breathing exercises (deep slow breathing with the diaphragm) the central white area gets whiter and the surrounding areas get redder. He likes to charge himself up with direct sunlight and is truly "solar powered."

Chapter 3-2. Hank posing with his twelve-pound bowling ball after completing three games at age 100 (December 1999). Between ages 93 and 99 he maintained a bowling average in the 150s. Hank was declared to be terminally ill with heart failure in 1991 with an enlarged heart as big as his chest on X-ray. His cardiologist gave him two days to live. He also suffered from a long list of diseases of physical degeneration including psoriasis over half of his body and getting up to urinate six time at night. All of these conditions cleared on a program including the anal heater once a week and a biochemist's nutritional program. He was done in by an intern's prescribing error when he was 100.

Chapter 4-1. Kathy Ryan drinking a glass of water with one hand without a tremor or spilling seven days after her first treatment with Rodger. Both arms were paralyzed for over 7 months following surgery for a benign brain tumor. In the mirror a bald spot can be seen caused by X-ray treatments following surgery.

Chapter 5-1. Dr McGee holding the horse anal heater that relieved "Pinky's" giant hives in 1995. Rodger on left. Veterinarians later told me the heater was larger than needed, but this was what Rodger dreamed up in his mind unassisted.

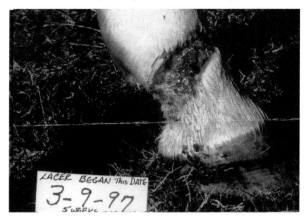

LACER BEGAN This DATE
3-9-97
SURFACE

Chapter 5-2. Front leg of a horse named "Dude" that got tangled in barbed wire and tore off a full thickness piece of skin about 4 by 8 inches. On 3-9-97, after 5 weeks of routine veterinary care, there were no signs of healing.

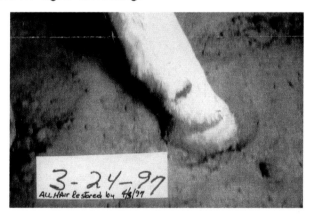

3-24-97
ALL HAIr Restored by 4/8/97

Chapter 5-3. Dude's wound was treated with a pulsed infrared LED pad set on Nogier's frequency A twice daily for 15 minutes. Healing is almost complete in 15 days (3-24-97). 10 days later all hair had grown back. Speed of healing is remarkable (hoof is buried in sand).

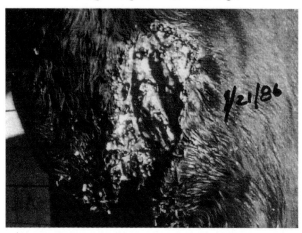

Chapter 5-4. Mare with two-day old barbed wire injury with area of skin missing measuring 18 by 8 inches and muscle exposed. Wound was treated with pulsed LEDs and pulsed low-level laser.

Chapter 5-5. Same wound 45 days later. Skin grew back in from edges and injury has healed completely with normal scar. No stiches were used, the safest choice in old, dirty wounds.

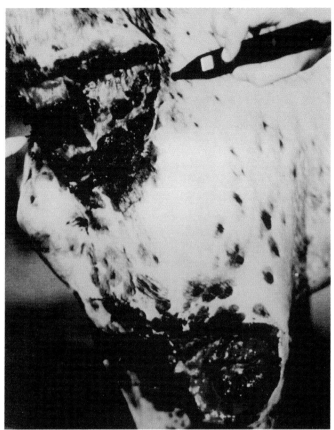

Chapter 5-6. Colt of mare shown in **5-4** that is assumed to have run into the same barbed wire fence at the same time as his mother. Wounds on neck and upper left front leg were treated with a pulsed infrared LED device and pulsed cold laser (the instruments seen in the photo). Photo was taken on the first day of treatment. Dark areas around wounds are dried blood.

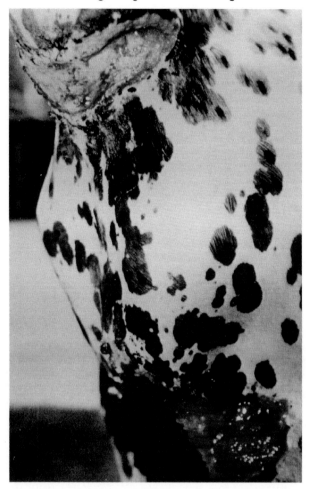

Chapter 5-7. Same colt two weeks later. Wounds are closing in and appear clean with granulation tissue, a normal part of the healing process.

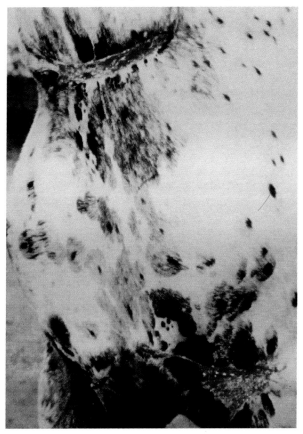

Chapter 5-8. Same colt 4 weeks after injury. Wounds are healing nicely and are substantially smaller. Photos **5-4** through **5-8** courtesy of Howard Mitchell DVM of Bristow, Oklahoma.

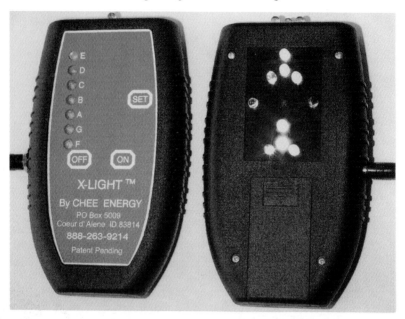

Chapter 6-1. 2003 version of the hand-held LED device, the **X-Light** with red, white blue, and infrared diodes. Several qigong masters say the instrument emits energy very close to chi itself. Most people can feel energy from the instrument on the palm from inches away as well as passing through a lead shield. Frequencies of Nogier can be selected for specific energy balancing treatments. By turning the device on and off the user can select one of three color options, 1) red, white, blue, and infrared, 2) red and infrared, or 3) blue alone.

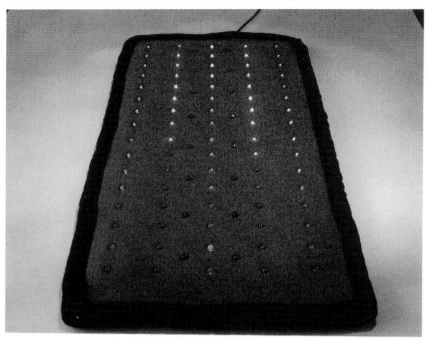

Chapter 6-2. 2002 version of the *Energy-Balancer,* a flexible blanket of red, white and blue LEDs arranged in rows to lie over energy meridians of the back and front of the chest. Many people feel energy tingling through the body when the LEDs are turned on. The device has an excellent record in treating back pain but can be used for many other situations.

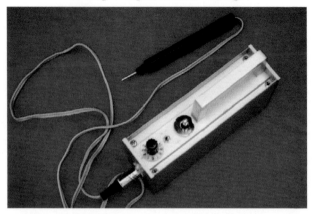

Chapter 7-1. *Punctoscope* developed by Dr. Paul Nogier purchased by Dr. McGee in 1975 in Lyon, France.

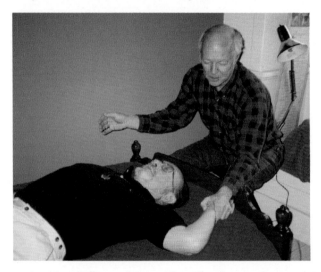

Chapter 7-2. Simulation of how Dr. Nogier performed his pulse test. Thumb of examiner's left hand detects changes in the radial pulse as items held in examiner's right hand are brought into the energy field of the patient by approaching the ear.

Chapter 9-1. Qigong masters Hu and Rodger, January 2000.

Appendix V-1. Dr McGee on left, Professor Lu Zuyin, professor of physics at the Institute for High Energy Physics, Beijing, in middle, world famous qigong master Yan Xin on right (1990).